Richardson Family,

Consider this your dependable co-pilot when it comes to tracking all of your cat's health and dental concerns that may arise. If all else fails, a good belly rub and chin scratch usually does the trick! Wishing you and your new feline family member good health and many PURRS of happiness!

Thom, Cindy, Parker, Stephane, Tandoori and Keanu

April 2023

TABLE OF CONTENTS

This Journal is for informational and archival purposes only and is not intended to treat, cure, diagnose or prevent illness or disease. You understand that this book is not intended as a substitute for a consultation with a licensed professional. Please consult with your own veterinarian or healthcare specialist regarding any suggestions and recommendations included in this book.

The publisher and the authors are providing this content on an "as is" basis and make no representations or warranties of any kind with respect to this book or its contents. The publisher and the authors disclaim all such representations and warranties, including but not limited to warranties of healthcare for a particular purpose. In addition, the publisher and the authors assume no responsibility for errors, inaccuracies, omissions, or any other inconsistencies herein.

The publisher and the authors make no guarantees concerning the level of success you may experience by following the practices and techniques in this book, and you accept the responsibility and understand that results will differ for each individual.

This book contains affiliate links, which means the author receives a small commission at no cost to you if you purchase through a link.

Published by Pet Tech Productions, Inc. | PO Box 2285 Carlsbad, CA, 92018 | www.PetTech.net

ISBN: 978-1-959498-00-1   Book and cover design by: www.Sebastian.Solutions   Printed by Amazon Kindle Direct   Made in the USA

ABOUT

Pet Tech, located in Carlsbad, CA, is the first international training center dedicated to providing Pet CPR, First Aid, Care and Safety trainings. The company was founded in 1996 by Thom Somes, The Pet Safety Guy™ and Cindy Buzas. Since 1997, the Pet Tech family of Instructors have been training pet lovers and Pet Care Professionals in the United States, Mexico, Canada, England, Australia, New Zealand, Singapore and Japan.

Our mission is ***Improving the Quality of Pets' Lives, One Pet Parent at a Time.***™ with the overall objective of ***Preventing 1 Million Pet ER Visits!***™ We teach pet parents and Pet Care Professionals how to care for their pets in emergency and in health so they have a happier, healthier and longer relationship with their furry four-legged family members. To date, we have trained 200,000 pet lovers and are on our way to 1 Million!

As the premier Pet CPR, First Aid & Care program, we are continually raising the bar of Pet Care Professionalism while exceeding industry standards.

The PetSaver Training has saved pets' lives and changed pet parents' lives around the world! Now we are excited to share this Pet Tech Feline Health Journal which will increases the quality and quantity of pets' lives and will strengthen the bond with your pets.

Be the Ultimate Pet Parent with the PetSaver™ Class

Don't let your furry family members fall victim to accident or illness. Become the ultimate pet parent and sign up for a PetSaver™ class to learn Pet CPR, First Aid & Care.

Visit or website for more information and to sign up for a class today.

www.PetTech.net

NEWS AND EVENTS

Throughout the year we have events and more to promote pet health and care. Be sure to visit and follow our blog for updates: **www.PetTech.net/blog**

PET TECH APP

You can also get the Pet Tech app for iOS and Android to stay in the loop! Visit the app store and search for Pet Tech or scan the QR code now.

Apple iOS   Android

WELCOME

Thank you for joining the Pet Tech Family of Pet Parents and Pet Care Professionals. We believe that all pets come in to our lives to teach us life lessons and be our companion on our journey together.

Oreo

The Pet Tech pet family started with Oreo, our black and white English Springer Spaniel, the original demo-dog extraordinaire. She was our inspiration in developing the pet CPR and first aid programs. Every skill we teach today was practiced on Oreo first (except compressions, never practice compressions on a live animal)!

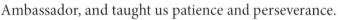
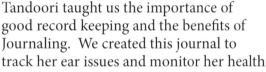
Duncan

Duncan, Oreo's son, was diagnosed with autoimmune hemolytic anemia when he was only 6 years old and was given 3 months to live. We learned the value of the healing power of nutrition, supplementation and home care. He lived an additional 16 months and helped us develop "Knowing Your Pets' Health: An Optimal Guide to Health and Wellness."

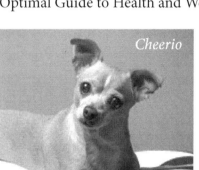
Cheerio

Cheerio our 11 pound Chihuahua was our traveling "laptop" companion as we toured the country promoting and teaching Pet Tech. He was the Pet Tech "Good Will" Ambassador, and taught us patience and perseverance.

Tandoori taught us the importance of good record keeping and the benefits of Journaling. We created this journal to track her ear issues and monitor her health both at home and with her vet. we also wanted to chronicle her life journey so we included sections to record her milestones and activities for the year!

Tandoori

Keanu

Keanu, the Pet Tech Corporate Cat, has his own Feline Health Journal. He started out in the mountains of Northern California in Big Foot country and now he resides at the beach. Rivalry with Tandoori on who sells the most journals. Keanu asks that you get 9... One for each life, ha-ha!

We appreciate your commitment to *Improving the quality of your cat's life ... one Journal entry at a time.* We wish you and your furry family members a happy and healthy journey on the trail of life.

Follow us social media and share your stories!

 Facebook.com/PetTech.Inc   Instagram.com/PetTechOfficial

MY CAT'S PROFILE

Photo Here

Pet Name

Breed

Color

Age

DOB

Weight

Gender ___ Male ___ Female

Spayed/Neutered ___ Yes ___ No

Adoption Info

Microchip Number

License Number

Allergies

Personality & Quirks

Exercise & Activities

Likes

Dislikes

Favorite Toys

Other

MY CAT'S PROFILE

Food Types ☐ Raw ☐ Kibble/Dry ☐ Home Cooked ☐ Canned ☐ Frozen ☐ Dehydrated ☐ Other

Food Brand(s)

Water Type ☐ Tap ☐ Filtered ☐ Other

Treats

Dietary Restrictions

Supplements

Flea & Tick Medications

Kitty Litter Type ☐ Clay ☐ Organic ☐ Other

Additional Medication   Dose / Freq.

Additional Medication   Dose / Freq.

Additional Medication   Dose / Freq.

Additional Medication   Dose / Freq.

Medical Issues / Conditions

Vaccine	Immunization Dates	Veterinarian
☐ Panleukopenia		
☐ Feline Calicivirus		
☐ Rabies		
☐ Viral Rhinotracheitis		
☐ Coronavirus		
☐ Bordetella		
☐ Snakebite		

VET & INSURANCE

Veterinarian Name

Phone	Email

Address

Animal Hospital

Phone	Email

Address

Insurance Company

Representative

Phone	Email

Policy #

Issue Date	Renewal/Expiration

Questions to ask before getting Pet Health Insurance.

1. Does the coverage exclude preexisting conditions?

2. Does the coverage exclude congenital disorders?

3. Is there a waiting period before coverage starts?

4. Is there a deductible?

5. Is there a lifetime or annual cap?

6. Does the company reimburse me or pay the Veterinarian?

Notes

DAILY ROUTINE

Feeding Routine

Morning Time	Food Amount	Water Amount
Afternoon Time	Food Amount	Water Amount
Evening Time	Food Amount	Water Amount

Amount of Treats / How Often

Potty Routine/Habits

Location(s) / Times

Play Time & Exercise

How Much

What Kind

How Often

Hygiene

Teeth Brushing

Coat Brushing

Ear Care

Nail Care

Eye Care

Naps & Sleep Habits

Favorite Napping Spot

Nighttime Sleeping Spot

Other

MY PET EMERGENCY PLAN

Wherever you live there are potential natural and man-made disasters. Therefore, we recommend you contact your local Animal Control, Neighborhood Watch, Fire Department, Police Station and/or FEMA for information on preparing your Home Emergency Plan. You should have at least two exits from your home; a specific place to meet outside and someone should be assigned responsibility for the family pet(s). It is recommended you practice your emergency plan twice a year. Schedule a practice in the Spring and one in the Fall. Be sure to check the batteries in your smoke and carbon monoxide detectors every six months.

1. Create and test your family communication plan.
2. Emergency Plans should include pets and Pet Care Professionals.
3. Choose a meeting place for family members.
4. Sign up for alerts and warnings.
5. Compile and safeguard important documents for you, your family and your pets.
6. Plan with neighbors and your community.
7. Designate an out-of-town contact.
8. Know and practice evacuation routes from home and city.
9. Household information and important contact numbers.
10. Gather and update emergency supplies including First Aid Kits (human and pet).
    Visit our website for Pet First Aid Kit contents: www.PetTech.net/petfirstaidkit or scan code

Emergency Contacts

Name	Relation
Phone	Email
Address	

Name	Relation
Phone	Email
Address	

Name	Relation
Phone	Email
Address	

Notes/Special Instructions

MY PET CARE PROFESSIONALS

Service Type

Name

Phone

Email

Address

Notes

Service Type

Name

Phone

Email

Address

Notes

Service Type

Name

Phone

Email

Address

Notes

Service Type

Name

Phone

Email

Address

Notes

CONNECT THE DOTS

COLORING PAGE

TOP 8 FUN CAT FACTS

1

Cats are believed to be the only mammals who don't taste sweetness.

2

Cats have up to 100 different vocalizations! While dogs only have 10.

3

Cats can jump up to six times their length.

4

Cats have nearly twice the amount of neurons in their cerebral cortex as dogs.

5

The first known cat video was recorded in 1894.

6

Cats have whiskers on the backs of their front legs, as well.

7

Some cats are ambidextrous, but 40% are either left or right pawed.

8

Despite popular belief, many cats are actually lactose intolerant.

FIRST AID QUIZ

1 Pet First Aid is the immediate care given to a cat who is injured or suddenly takes ill.

☐ True ☐ False

2 All human medicines will work on cats if you adjust the dosage for their weight.

☐ True ☐ False

3 As a general rule, a cats normal temperature ranges from 100.4º to 102.5º F.

☐ True ☐ False

4 Pet CPR is best learned with hands-on training and skills practice.

☐ True ☐ False

5 Rescue Breathing is warranted when your pet has no heart beat and no breathing.

☐ True ☐ False

6 The Primary Pet Assessment includes the skills and techniques necessary for Pet CPR, First Aid and Rescue Breathing.

☐ True ☐ False

7 If you suspect your cat is poisoned, it's important to immediately get your cat to the vet, as well as know what and how much poison was ingested.

☐ True ☐ False

8 The Black Widow Spider bite is virtually harmless to cats.

☐ True ☐ False

9 Death by poisoning is one of the least common preventable pet accidents.

☐ True ☐ False

10 Baby snake venom is as venomous as their parent's venom.

☐ True ☐ False

11 Lilies are not one of the many plants that are poisonous to your cats.

☐ True ☐ False

Check your answers on page 104!

CAT TRAITS WORD SEARCH

```
G A A W C B U T M V K C M U Y J F Q K E
J I T V L O G C D K S V A I P P X R P J
E Q N U W E C Z E V C N C H E S H I R E
Z U V Q Q C A N T A N K E R O U S P C D
R E L P U P A U F R K Z S J O A H D W V
E E D R V I X K U G B S N K P L R E Y X
L N O U E N S A L A J T F F I M I V Z X
S S M I F K G I B R L R J A E T U J J J
P R I Y R P Q S T F M E Y T W R T R J W
O O N G I A W G R I P E V F A A B I B M
N O A R E N H R E V T Y D I G P V S M S
T U N U N T W S K L R E H P Z D E P V H
A T T M D H T M T D K P Q M I O D Q S E
N G W P L E W H R H A S N S L I M C D
E O H Y Y R O W A U H J I E V L G R R E
O I Q S N A K Q C M R T T N P H R E A U
U N N A H V L E K A L W I S I U E I T A
S G Q W J P R P E N X Z X Z Z C E I C Z
N K X I G Z Q B R T L V B Q W S K Y H D
C S F V H U N T E R A H D O T K A Y Y Y
```

1. Pedigree
2. Street
3. Ragdoll
4. Queen
5. Human
6. Hunter
7. Cantankerous
8. Inquisitive
9. Skittish
10. Grumpy
11. Dominant
12. Friendly
13. Spontaneous
14. Pink Panther
15. Scratchy
16. Tracker
17. Garfield
18. Finicky
19. Cheshire
20. Outgoing

Answer key on page 104.

SPOT 8 DIFFERENCES

Answer key on page 104.

KITTY MAZE

Answer key on page 105.

FIND THE 6 CATS!

Answer key on page 105.

KITTY ADOPTION LOGIC PUZZLE

Yesterday, five different people adopted cats from Fur Family Animal Sanctuary. The cats were all different breeds and different ages, and each cat received a unique name.

DIRECTIONS: Use the clues and the grid below to help you match each person to their cat, including the breed of cat they adopted, the age of their cat, and the name of their cat.

CLUES:
- Ashley did not name her cat Duke, nor is her cat five years old.
- The four-year-old cat was not named Otto.
- Gus, who is one year old, is not a Persian.
- Vijay named his cat Jax, and Lamar named his cat Duke.
- Neither Ashley nor Lamar adopted a Ragdoll.
- Russell adopted a Main Coon.
- Otto, who is a Scottish Fold, is not two years old.
- The Exotic Shorthair is the oldest cat, and the Ragdoll is the youngest cat.
- Lamar's cat is two years old.

		BREED OF CAT				AGE OF CAT					NAME OF CAT				
		Main Coon	Exotic Shorthair	Persian	Ragdoll	Scottish Fold	1 year old	2 years old	3 years old	4 years old	5 years old	Duke	Gus	Jax	Otto	Ruby
PERSON	Ashley															
	Kimi															
	Lamar															
	Russell															
	Vijay															
NAME OF CAT	Duke															
	Gus															
	Jax															
	Otto															
	Ruby															
AGE OF CAT	1 year old															
	2 years old															
	3 years old															
	4 years old															
	5 years old															

Answer key on page 105.

SNOUT-TO-TAIL™ WORD SCRAMBLE

The Snout-To-Tail Wellness Assessment is the best way to determining the current status of a cat's overall health. We'll tell you how to do the full Snout-To-Tail Wellness Assessment on the next page (22), but try your best to unscramble the areas we cover here first. To help you out, we've done the first one for you!

ONTSU & ELZUZM

Snout and Muzzle

UMSG & TEHET

ESEY

LLUKS

ERAS

ECNK & SPNIE

TCHSE & BRIS

ROFNT SGEL & PASW

KSACB ESGL & ASWP

AOENBDM

KNIS NAD CATO

AITL

Answer key on page 105.

SNOUT-TO-TAIL™ ASSESSMENT

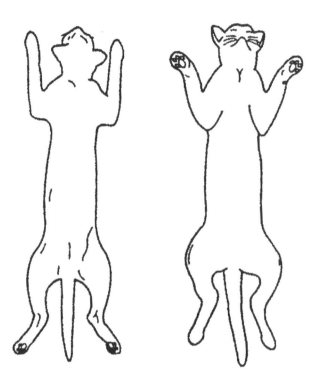

The Snout-To-Tail Wellness Assessment is a systematic and deliberate method for evaluating and determining the current status of a cat's overall health. If you know what is "normal" for the cat, then you will be able to quickly recognize what's "NOT normal." Early detection means early intervention.

Each assessment can take a few minutes or as long as it takes you to complete all the steps. You should assess the cat from Snout-To-Tail daily or at a minimum once a week. It should be done the same way each time with deliberate intent and purpose. You will be looking for any irregularities of the skin or hair coat, bumps, lumps, pain response, swelling, heat, rashes, secretions or any changes from the last assessment.

As a pet parent, you need to observe and assess the cat with a clinical eye. The Snout-To-Tail Wellness Assessment is the best way to create a baseline and "keep an eye" on a their health and wellbeing.

Physical Stance: How does the cat look as it stands and sits from all angles, walking on the leash or sleeping in the warm afternoon sun?

Food and Water: One of the first signs of something not being right with a cat is a change in its eating and drinking habits. Is it eating or drinking more than usual or not at all? Does it sit and drool at the food? This could be a sign of a toothache or other medical issues.

Skin and Coat: One of the first indicators of an animal affected with disease or malnutrition is the skin and hair coat. Is the skin dry, have irritations or dandruff? Has the coat dramatically changed? Is it shedding more than normal for the time of year? Is the pet excessively chewing, scratching or licking?

Find a quiet place free of distractions for you and your cat. They can be in a sitting position with you on their side. The following outlines the steps in the Snout-To-Tail Wellness Assessment™, including a description of items to take notice of, and all concerns should be recorded with time and date on the Snout-To-Tail Worksheets included in this Pet Tech Feline Health Journal.

You should discuss any abnormalities or changes in the cat's assessment with the veterinarian as soon as possible to determine the proper course of action or if any care or treatment is necessary.

In addition to being a part of your cat's daily health routine, the S2T is also a fun and bonding experience for you and your cat. As a Pet Parent, there is no part of your cat that you should not be able to touch. And, if your cat is comfortable being touched it will assure a better examination by the veterinarian, a groom by the groomer and a visit by the pet sitter.

Start Positive… Stay Positive… End Positive!

SNOUT-TO-TAIL™ ASSESSMENT

Snout & Muzzle: The nose should not be so wet that there is discharge, or so dry that it is cracked.

Gums & Teeth: The gums should be bubble-gum pink (unless they normally have black gums like a Chow) and the teeth white with no bad odor.

Eyes: The eyes should be clear with no discharge and they should track movement. Pupils should be equal and respond to light.

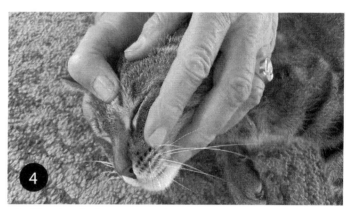

Skull: Check the crown/skull of the head for heat, abrasions, bumps or any pain response.

Ears: The ears should not have any odor, discharge or waxy buildup and should not be sensitive or painful to the touch.

Neck & Spine: Going over the head, check the neck and spine for abrasions, bumps, masses, tenderness or sores. Anchoring the spine at the neck with one hand, slide the other hand along the spine to the base of the tail.

SNOUT-TO-TAIL™ ASSESSMENT

Chest & Ribs: You should be able to easily feel the ribs under the fur coat. The pet's breathing should be smooth, rhythmic and easy. Check the front of the pet's chest too.

Front Legs & Paws: Note the range of use and movement of each leg. The dew claws and nails should not be cracked, split or painful. Gently check between the toes and pads for foreign bodies, torn pads or excessive hair.

Back Legs & Paws: Check each of the hind legs and paws by following the same procedure as the front legs and paws.

Abdomen: Palpate the abdomen which should not be sensitive, painful or rigid. Check the mammary glands and genitals. There should be no colored discharge. The anal area should be free of hair, debris and feces.

Skin & Coat: The skin and coat should be appraised throughout your assessment for texture, color, temperature, excessive shedding and quality of haircoat.

Tail: The tail should be examined for deformity or pain and range of use and movement.

SNOUT-TO-TAIL™ WORKSHEET

Date	Weight	Coat Color
Pulse	Temp	Breathing

Notes / Describe Issues

Photo Here

1	Snout & Muzzle	Good	Dry, Cracked or Discharge
2	Gums & Teeth	Good	Discoloration, Odor or Tartar
3	Eyes	Good	Clear, Hazy or Discharge
	Whites of Eyes	White	Red Yellow
4	Skull	Good	Bumps, Lumps or Pain/Sensitivity
5	Ears	Good	Odor, Discharge or Sensitive
6	Neck & Spine	Good	Lumps, Sores or Pain/Sensitivity
7	Chest & Ribs	Good	Lumps, Sores or Pain/Sensitivity
8	Front Legs & Paws	Good	Range, Cracked Pads or Broken Nails
9	Back Legs & Paws	Good	Range, Cracked Pads or Broken Nails
10	Abdomen	Good	Rigid, Pain/Odor Discharge Pain
	Genitals / Glands	Good	Rigid, Pain/Odor Discharge Pain
	Anal Area	Good	Hair, Debris or Feces
11	Skin & Coat	Good	Dry, Hairloss, Hot Spots or Bumps
12	Tail	Good	Deformity, Range of Use

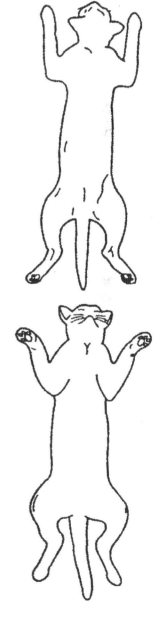

SNOUT-TO-TAIL™ WORKSHEET

Date	Weight	Coat Color
Pulse	Temp	Breathing

Notes / Describe Issues

Photo Here

#	Area		Good		Issue
1	Snout & Muzzle	☐	Good	☐	Dry, Cracked or Discharge
2	Gums & Teeth	☐	Good	☐	Discoloration, Odor or Tartar
3	Eyes	☐	Good	☐	Clear, Hazy or Discharge
	Whites of Eyes	☐	White	☐ Red	☐ Yellow
4	Skull	☐	Good	☐	Bumps, Lumps or Pain/Sensitivity
5	Ears	☐	Good	☐	Odor, Discharge or Sensitive
6	Neck & Spine	☐	Good	☐	Lumps, Sores or Pain/Sensitivity
7	Chest & Ribs	☐	Good	☐	Lumps, Sores or Pain/Sensitivity
8	Front Legs & Paws	☐	Good	☐	Range, Cracked Pads or Broken Nails
9	Back Legs & Paws	☐	Good	☐	Range, Cracked Pads or Broken Nails
10	Abdomen	☐	Good	☐	Rigid, Pain/Odor Discharge Pain
	Genitals / Glands	☐	Good	☐	Rigid, Pain/Odor Discharge Pain
	Anal Area	☐	Good	☐	Hair, Debris or Feces
11	Skin & Coat	☐	Good	☐	Dry, Hairloss, Hot Spots or Bumps
12	Tail	☐	Good	☐	Deformity, Range of Use

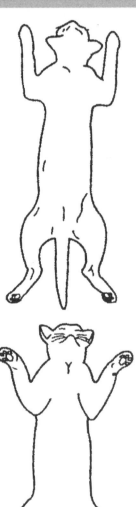

Indicate issue area(s).

SNOUT-TO-TAIL™ WORKSHEET

Date	Weight	Coat Color
Pulse	Temp	Breathing

Notes / Describe Issues

Photo Here

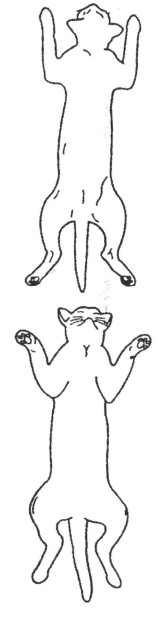

1	Snout & Muzzle	Good		Dry, Cracked or Discharge	
2	Gums & Teeth	Good		Discoloration, Odor or Tartar	
3	Eyes	Good		Clear, Hazy or Discharge	
	Whites of Eyes	White	Red		Yellow
4	Skull	Good		Bumps, Lumps or Pain/Sensitivity	
5	Ears	Good		Odor, Discharge or Sensitive	
6	Neck & Spine	Good		Lumps, Sores or Pain/Sensitivity	
7	Chest & Ribs	Good		Lumps, Sores or Pain/Sensitivity	
8	Front Legs & Paws	Good		Range, Cracked Pads or Broken Nails	
9	Back Legs & Paws	Good		Range, Cracked Pads or Broken Nails	
10	Abdomen	Good		Rigid, Pain/Odor Discharge Pain	
	Genitals / Glands	Good		Rigid, Pain/Odor Discharge Pain	
	Anal Area	Good		Hair, Debris or Feces	
11	Skin & Coat	Good		Dry, Hairloss, Hot Spots or Bumps	
12	Tail	Good		Deformity, Range of Use	

SNOUT-TO-TAIL™ WORKSHEET

Date	Weight	Coat Color
Pulse	Temp	Breathing

Notes / Describe Issues

Photo Here

#	Area	Good	Issue
1	Snout & Muzzle	☐ Good	☐ Dry, Cracked or Discharge
2	Gums & Teeth	☐ Good	☐ Discoloration, Odor or Tartar
3	Eyes	☐ Good	☐ Clear, Hazy or Discharge
	Whites of Eyes	☐ White	☐ Red ☐ Yellow
4	Skull	☐ Good	☐ Bumps, Lumps or Pain/Sensitivity
5	Ears	☐ Good	☐ Odor, Discharge or Sensitive
6	Neck & Spine	☐ Good	☐ Lumps, Sores or Pain/Sensitivity
7	Chest & Ribs	☐ Good	☐ Lumps, Sores or Pain/Sensitivity
8	Front Legs & Paws	☐ Good	☐ Range, Cracked Pads or Broken Nails
9	Back Legs & Paws	☐ Good	☐ Range, Cracked Pads or Broken Nails
10	Abdomen	☐ Good	☐ Rigid, Pain/Odor Discharge Pain
	Genitals / Glands	☐ Good	☐ Rigid, Pain/Odor Discharge Pain
	Anal Area	☐ Good	☐ Hair, Debris or Feces
11	Skin & Coat	☐ Good	☐ Dry, Hairloss, Hot Spots or Bumps
12	Tail	☐ Good	☐ Deformity, Range of Use

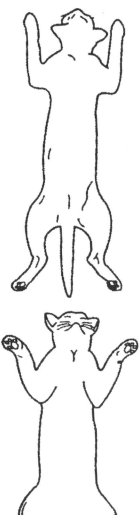

Indicate issue area(s).

SNOUT-TO-TAIL™ WORKSHEET

Date	Weight	Coat Color
Pulse	Temp	Breathing

Notes / Describe Issues

Photo Here

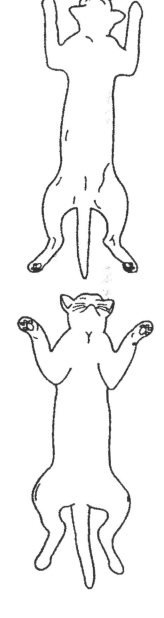

1	Snout & Muzzle	Good		Dry, Cracked or Discharge
2	Gums & Teeth	Good		Discoloration, Odor or Tartar
3	Eyes	Good		Clear, Hazy or Discharge
	Whites of Eyes	White	Red	Yellow
4	Skull	Good		Bumps, Lumps or Pain/Sensitivity
5	Ears	Good		Odor, Discharge or Sensitive
6	Neck & Spine	Good		Lumps, Sores or Pain/Sensitivity
7	Chest & Ribs	Good		Lumps, Sores or Pain/Sensitivity
8	Front Legs & Paws	Good		Range, Cracked Pads or Broken Nails
9	Back Legs & Paws	Good		Range, Cracked Pads or Broken Nails
10	Abdomen	Good		Rigid, Pain/Odor Discharge Pain
	Genitals / Glands	Good		Rigid, Pain/Odor Discharge Pain
	Anal Area	Good		Hair, Debris or Feces
11	Skin & Coat	Good		Dry, Hairloss, Hot Spots or Bumps
12	Tail	Good		Deformity, Range of Use

SNOUT-TO-TAIL™ WORKSHEET

Date	Weight	Coat Color
Pulse	Temp	Breathing

Notes / Describe Issues

Photo Here

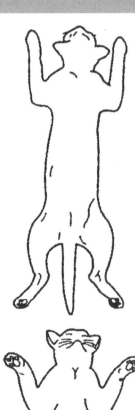

1	Snout & Muzzle	☐ Good	☐ Dry, Cracked or Discharge
2	Gums & Teeth	☐ Good	☐ Discoloration, Odor or Tartar
3	Eyes	☐ Good	☐ Clear, Hazy or Discharge
	Whites of Eyes	☐ White	☐ Red ☐ Yellow
4	Skull	☐ Good	☐ Bumps, Lumps or Pain/Sensitivity
5	Ears	☐ Good	☐ Odor, Discharge or Sensitive
6	Neck & Spine	☐ Good	☐ Lumps, Sores or Pain/Sensitivity
7	Chest & Ribs	☐ Good	☐ Lumps, Sores or Pain/Sensitivity
8	Front Legs & Paws	☐ Good	☐ Range, Cracked Pads or Broken Nails
9	Back Legs & Paws	☐ Good	☐ Range, Cracked Pads or Broken Nails
10	Abdomen	☐ Good	☐ Rigid, Pain/Odor Discharge Pain
	Genitals / Glands	☐ Good	☐ Rigid, Pain/Odor Discharge Pain
	Anal Area	☐ Good	☐ Hair, Debris or Feces
11	Skin & Coat	☐ Good	☐ Dry, Hairloss, Hot Spots or Bumps
12	Tail	☐ Good	☐ Deformity, Range of Use

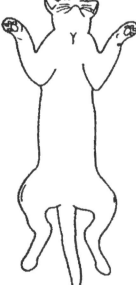

Indicate issue area(s).

SNOUT-TO-TAIL™ WORKSHEET

Date	Weight	Coat Color
Pulse	Temp	Breathing

Notes / Describe Issues

Photo Here

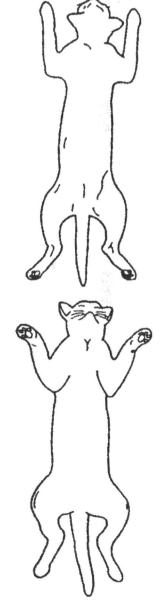

1	Snout & Muzzle	Good	Dry, Cracked or Discharge
2	Gums & Teeth	Good	Discoloration, Odor or Tartar
3	Eyes	Good	Clear, Hazy or Discharge
	Whites of Eyes	White	Red Yellow
4	Skull	Good	Bumps, Lumps or Pain/Sensitivity
5	Ears	Good	Odor, Discharge or Sensitive
6	Neck & Spine	Good	Lumps, Sores or Pain/Sensitivity
7	Chest & Ribs	Good	Lumps, Sores or Pain/Sensitivity
8	Front Legs & Paws	Good	Range, Cracked Pads or Broken Nails
9	Back Legs & Paws	Good	Range, Cracked Pads or Broken Nails
10	Abdomen	Good	Rigid, Pain/Odor Discharge Pain
	Genitals / Glands	Good	Rigid, Pain/Odor Discharge Pain
	Anal Area	Good	Hair, Debris or Feces
11	Skin & Coat	Good	Dry, Hairloss, Hot Spots or Bumps
12	Tail	Good	Deformity, Range of Use

SNOUT-TO-TAIL™ WORKSHEET

Date	Weight	Coat Color
Pulse	Temp	Breathing

Notes / Describe Issues

Photo Here

#					
1	Snout & Muzzle	☐ Good	☐ Dry, Cracked or Discharge		
2	Gums & Teeth	☐ Good	☐ Discoloration, Odor or Tartar		
3	Eyes	☐ Good	☐ Clear, Hazy or Discharge		
	Whites of Eyes	☐ White	☐ Red	☐ Yellow	
4	Skull	☐ Good	☐ Bumps, Lumps or Pain/Sensitivity		
5	Ears	☐ Good	☐ Odor, Discharge or Sensitive		
6	Neck & Spine	☐ Good	☐ Lumps, Sores or Pain/Sensitivity		
7	Chest & Ribs	☐ Good	☐ Lumps, Sores or Pain/Sensitivity		
8	Front Legs & Paws	☐ Good	☐ Range, Cracked Pads or Broken Nails		
9	Back Legs & Paws	☐ Good	☐ Range, Cracked Pads or Broken Nails		
10	Abdomen	☐ Good	☐ Rigid, Pain/Odor Discharge Pain		
	Genitals / Glands	☐ Good	☐ Rigid, Pain/Odor Discharge Pain		
	Anal Area	☐ Good	☐ Hair, Debris or Feces		
11	Skin & Coat	☐ Good	☐ Dry, Hairloss, Hot Spots or Bumps		
12	Tail	☐ Good	☐ Deformity, Range of Use		

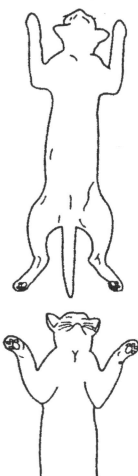

Indicate issue area(s).

SNOUT-TO-TAIL™ WORKSHEET

Date	Weight	Coat Color
Pulse	Temp	Breathing

Notes / Describe Issues

Photo Here

1	Snout & Muzzle	Good		Dry, Cracked or Discharge
2	Gums & Teeth	Good		Discoloration, Odor or Tartar
3	Eyes	Good		Clear, Hazy or Discharge
	Whites of Eyes	White	Red	Yellow
4	Skull	Good		Bumps, Lumps or Pain/Sensitivity
5	Ears	Good		Odor, Discharge or Sensitive
6	Neck & Spine	Good		Lumps, Sores or Pain/Sensitivity
7	Chest & Ribs	Good		Lumps, Sores or Pain/Sensitivity
8	Front Legs & Paws	Good		Range, Cracked Pads or Broken Nails
9	Back Legs & Paws	Good		Range, Cracked Pads or Broken Nails
10	Abdomen	Good		Rigid, Pain/Odor Discharge Pain
	Genitals / Glands	Good		Rigid, Pain/Odor Discharge Pain
	Anal Area	Good		Hair, Debris or Feces
11	Skin & Coat	Good		Dry, Hairloss, Hot Spots or Bumps
12	Tail	Good		Deformity, Range of Use

SNOUT-TO-TAIL™ WORKSHEET

Date	Weight	Coat Color
Pulse	Temp	Breathing

Notes / Describe Issues

Photo Here

#			
1	Snout & Muzzle	Good	Dry, Cracked or Discharge
2	Gums & Teeth	Good	Discoloration, Odor or Tartar
3	Eyes	Good	Clear, Hazy or Discharge
	Whites of Eyes	White	Red Yellow
4	Skull	Good	Bumps, Lumps or Pain/Sensitivity
5	Ears	Good	Odor, Discharge or Sensitive
6	Neck & Spine	Good	Lumps, Sores or Pain/Sensitivity
7	Chest & Ribs	Good	Lumps, Sores or Pain/Sensitivity
8	Front Legs & Paws	Good	Range, Cracked Pads or Broken Nails
9	Back Legs & Paws	Good	Range, Cracked Pads or Broken Nails
10	Abdomen	Good	Rigid, Pain/Odor Discharge Pain
	Genitals / Glands	Good	Rigid, Pain/Odor Discharge Pain
	Anal Area	Good	Hair, Debris or Feces
11	Skin & Coat	Good	Dry, Hairloss, Hot Spots or Bumps
12	Tail	Good	Deformity, Range of Use

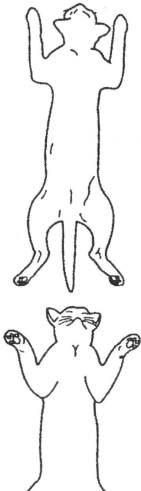

Indicate issue area(s).

SNOUT-TO-TAIL™ WORKSHEET

Date	Weight	Coat Color
Pulse	Temp	Breathing

Notes / Describe Issues

Photo Here

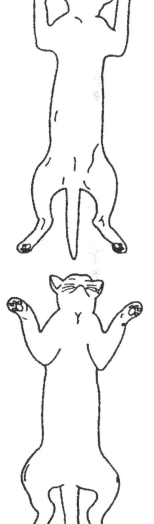

#	Area			
1	Snout & Muzzle	Good		Dry, Cracked or Discharge
2	Gums & Teeth	Good		Discoloration, Odor or Tartar
3	Eyes	Good		Clear, Hazy or Discharge
	Whites of Eyes	White	Red	Yellow
4	Skull	Good		Bumps, Lumps or Pain/Sensitivity
5	Ears	Good		Odor, Discharge or Sensitive
6	Neck & Spine	Good		Lumps, Sores or Pain/Sensitivity
7	Chest & Ribs	Good		Lumps, Sores or Pain/Sensitivity
8	Front Legs & Paws	Good		Range, Cracked Pads or Broken Nails
9	Back Legs & Paws	Good		Range, Cracked Pads or Broken Nails
10	Abdomen	Good		Rigid, Pain/Odor Discharge Pain
	Genitals / Glands	Good		Rigid, Pain/Odor Discharge Pain
	Anal Area	Good		Hair, Debris or Feces
11	Skin & Coat	Good		Dry, Hairloss, Hot Spots or Bumps
12	Tail	Good		Deformity, Range of Use

SNOUT-TO-TAIL™ WORKSHEET

Date	Weight	Coat Color
Pulse	Temp	Breathing

Notes / Describe Issues

Photo Here

#	Area	Good	Issue
1	Snout & Muzzle	Good	Dry, Cracked or Discharge
2	Gums & Teeth	Good	Discoloration, Odor or Tartar
3	Eyes	Good	Clear, Hazy or Discharge
	Whites of Eyes	White	Red Yellow
4	Skull	Good	Bumps, Lumps or Pain/Sensitivity
5	Ears	Good	Odor, Discharge or Sensitive
6	Neck & Spine	Good	Lumps, Sores or Pain/Sensitivity
7	Chest & Ribs	Good	Lumps, Sores or Pain/Sensitivity
8	Front Legs & Paws	Good	Range, Cracked Pads or Broken Nails
9	Back Legs & Paws	Good	Range, Cracked Pads or Broken Nails
10	Abdomen	Good	Rigid, Pain/Odor Discharge Pain
	Genitals / Glands	Good	Rigid, Pain/Odor Discharge Pain
	Anal Area	Good	Hair, Debris or Feces
11	Skin & Coat	Good	Dry, Hairloss, Hot Spots or Bumps
12	Tail	Good	Deformity, Range of Use

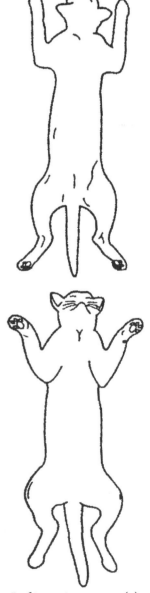

Indicate issue area(s).

SNOUT-TO-TAIL™ WORKSHEET

Date	Weight	Coat Color
Pulse	Temp	Breathing

Notes / Describe Issues

Photo Here

#		Good		
1	Snout & Muzzle	Good		Dry, Cracked or Discharge
2	Gums & Teeth	Good		Discoloration, Odor or Tartar
3	Eyes	Good		Clear, Hazy or Discharge
	Whites of Eyes	White	Red	Yellow
4	Skull	Good		Bumps, Lumps or Pain/Sensitivity
5	Ears	Good		Odor, Discharge or Sensitive
6	Neck & Spine	Good		Lumps, Sores or Pain/Sensitivity
7	Chest & Ribs	Good		Lumps, Sores or Pain/Sensitivity
8	Front Legs & Paws	Good		Range, Cracked Pads or Broken Nails
9	Back Legs & Paws	Good		Range, Cracked Pads or Broken Nails
10	Abdomen	Good		Rigid, Pain/Odor Discharge Pain
	Genitals / Glands	Good		Rigid, Pain/Odor Discharge Pain
	Anal Area	Good		Hair, Debris or Feces
11	Skin & Coat	Good		Dry, Hairloss, Hot Spots or Bumps
12	Tail	Good		Deformity, Range of Use

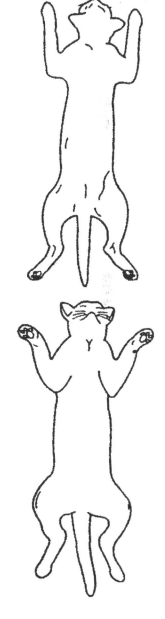

SNOUT-TO-TAIL™ WORKSHEET

Date	Weight	Coat Color
Pulse	Temp	Breathing

Notes / Describe Issues

Photo Here

#	Area		Good		Issue
1	Snout & Muzzle		Good		Dry, Cracked or Discharge
2	Gums & Teeth		Good		Discoloration, Odor or Tartar
3	Eyes		Good		Clear, Hazy or Discharge
	Whites of Eyes		White	Red	Yellow
4	Skull		Good		Bumps, Lumps or Pain/Sensitivity
5	Ears		Good		Odor, Discharge or Sensitive
6	Neck & Spine		Good		Lumps, Sores or Pain/Sensitivity
7	Chest & Ribs		Good		Lumps, Sores or Pain/Sensitivity
8	Front Legs & Paws		Good		Range, Cracked Pads or Broken Nails
9	Back Legs & Paws		Good		Range, Cracked Pads or Broken Nails
10	Abdomen		Good		Rigid, Pain/Odor Discharge Pain
	Genitals / Glands		Good		Rigid, Pain/Odor Discharge Pain
	Anal Area		Good		Hair, Debris or Feces
11	Skin & Coat		Good		Dry, Hairloss, Hot Spots or Bumps
12	Tail		Good		Deformity, Range of Use

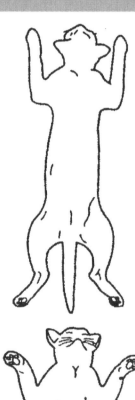

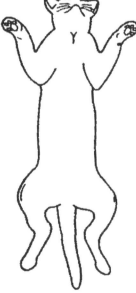

Indicate issue area(s).

SNOUT-TO-TAIL™ WORKSHEET

Date	Weight	Coat Color
Pulse	Temp	Breathing

Notes / Describe Issues

Photo Here

1	Snout & Muzzle	☐ Good	☐ Dry, Cracked or Discharge
2	Gums & Teeth	☐ Good	☐ Discoloration, Odor or Tartar
3	Eyes	☐ Good	☐ Clear, Hazy or Discharge
	Whites of Eyes	☐ White	☐ Red ☐ Yellow
4	Skull	☐ Good	☐ Bumps, Lumps or Pain/Sensitivity
5	Ears	☐ Good	☐ Odor, Discharge or Sensitive
6	Neck & Spine	☐ Good	☐ Lumps, Sores or Pain/Sensitivity
7	Chest & Ribs	☐ Good	☐ Lumps, Sores or Pain/Sensitivity
8	Front Legs & Paws	☐ Good	☐ Range, Cracked Pads or Broken Nails
9	Back Legs & Paws	☐ Good	☐ Range, Cracked Pads or Broken Nails
10	Abdomen	☐ Good	☐ Rigid, Pain/Odor Discharge Pain
	Genitals / Glands	☐ Good	☐ Rigid, Pain/Odor Discharge Pain
	Anal Area	☐ Good	☐ Hair, Debris or Feces
11	Skin & Coat	☐ Good	☐ Dry, Hairloss, Hot Spots or Bumps
12	Tail	☐ Good	☐ Deformity, Range of Use

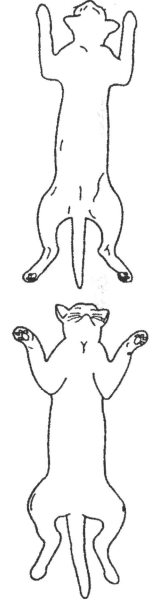

SNOUT-TO-TAIL™ WORKSHEET

Date	Weight	Coat Color
Pulse	Temp	Breathing

Notes / Describe Issues

Photo Here

#		Good		
1	Snout & Muzzle	Good	Dry, Cracked or Discharge
2	Gums & Teeth	Good	Discoloration, Odor or Tartar
3	Eyes	Good	Clear, Hazy or Discharge
	Whites of Eyes	White	Red	Yellow
4	Skull	Good	Bumps, Lumps or Pain/Sensitivity
5	Ears	Good	Odor, Discharge or Sensitive
6	Neck & Spine	Good	Lumps, Sores or Pain/Sensitivity
7	Chest & Ribs	Good	Lumps, Sores or Pain/Sensitivity
8	Front Legs & Paws	Good	Range, Cracked Pads or Broken Nails
9	Back Legs & Paws	Good	Range, Cracked Pads or Broken Nails
10	Abdomen	Good	Rigid, Pain/Odor Discharge Pain
	Genitals / Glands	Good	Rigid, Pain/Odor Discharge Pain
	Anal Area	Good	Hair, Debris or Feces
11	Skin & Coat	Good	Dry, Hairloss, Hot Spots or Bumps
12	Tail	Good	Deformity, Range of Use

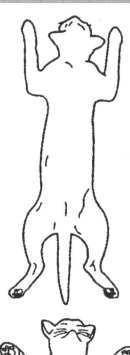

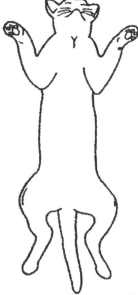

Indicate issue area(s).

SNOUT-TO-TAIL™ WORKSHEET

Date	Weight	Coat Color
Pulse	Temp	Breathing

Notes / Describe Issues

Photo Here

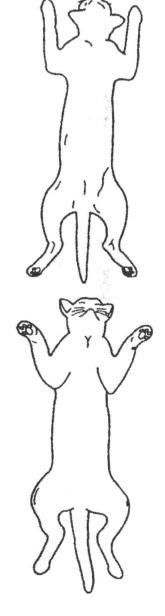

1	Snout & Muzzle	☐ Good	☐ Dry, Cracked or Discharge
2	Gums & Teeth	☐ Good	☐ Discoloration, Odor or Tartar
3	Eyes	☐ Good	☐ Clear, Hazy or Discharge
	Whites of Eyes	☐ White	☐ Red ☐ Yellow
4	Skull	☐ Good	☐ Bumps, Lumps or Pain/Sensitivity
5	Ears	☐ Good	☐ Odor, Discharge or Sensitive
6	Neck & Spine	☐ Good	☐ Lumps, Sores or Pain/Sensitivity
7	Chest & Ribs	☐ Good	☐ Lumps, Sores or Pain/Sensitivity
8	Front Legs & Paws	☐ Good	☐ Range, Cracked Pads or Broken Nails
9	Back Legs & Paws	☐ Good	☐ Range, Cracked Pads or Broken Nails
10	Abdomen	☐ Good	☐ Rigid, Pain/Odor Discharge Pain
	Genitals / Glands	☐ Good	☐ Rigid, Pain/Odor Discharge Pain
	Anal Area	☐ Good	☐ Hair, Debris or Feces
11	Skin & Coat	☐ Good	☐ Dry, Hairloss, Hot Spots or Bumps
12	Tail	☐ Good	☐ Deformity, Range of Use

SNOUT-TO-TAIL™ WORKSHEET

Date	Weight	Coat Color
Pulse	Temp	Breathing

Notes / Describe Issues

Photo Here

#					
1	Snout & Muzzle	☐ Good	☐ Dry, Cracked or Discharge		
2	Gums & Teeth	☐ Good	☐ Discoloration, Odor or Tartar		
3	Eyes	☐ Good	☐ Clear, Hazy or Discharge		
	Whites of Eyes	☐ White	☐ Red	☐ Yellow	
4	Skull	☐ Good	☐ Bumps, Lumps or Pain/Sensitivity		
5	Ears	☐ Good	☐ Odor, Discharge or Sensitive		
6	Neck & Spine	☐ Good	☐ Lumps, Sores or Pain/Sensitivity		
7	Chest & Ribs	☐ Good	☐ Lumps, Sores or Pain/Sensitivity		
8	Front Legs & Paws	☐ Good	☐ Range, Cracked Pads or Broken Nails		
9	Back Legs & Paws	☐ Good	☐ Range, Cracked Pads or Broken Nails		
10	Abdomen	☐ Good	☐ Rigid, Pain/Odor Discharge Pain		
	Genitals / Glands	☐ Good	☐ Rigid, Pain/Odor Discharge Pain		
	Anal Area	☐ Good	☐ Hair, Debris or Feces		
11	Skin & Coat	☐ Good	☐ Dry, Hairloss, Hot Spots or Bumps		
12	Tail	☐ Good	☐ Deformity, Range of Use		

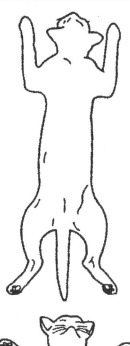

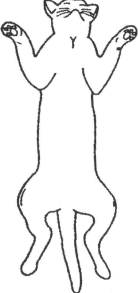

Indicate issue area(s).

SNOUT-TO-TAIL™ WORKSHEET

Date	Weight	Coat Color
Pulse	Temp	Breathing

Notes / Describe Issues

Photo Here

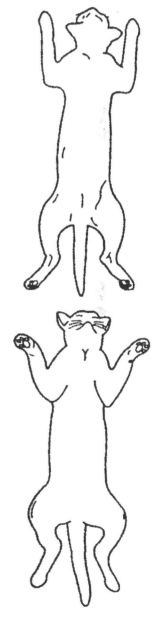

1	Snout & Muzzle	☐ Good	☐	Dry, Cracked or Discharge
2	Gums & Teeth	☐ Good	☐	Discoloration, Odor or Tartar
3	Eyes	☐ Good	☐	Clear, Hazy or Discharge
	Whites of Eyes	☐ White	☐ Red	☐ Yellow
4	Skull	☐ Good	☐	Bumps, Lumps or Pain/Sensitivity
5	Ears	☐ Good	☐	Odor, Discharge or Sensitive
6	Neck & Spine	☐ Good	☐	Lumps, Sores or Pain/Sensitivity
7	Chest & Ribs	☐ Good	☐	Lumps, Sores or Pain/Sensitivity
8	Front Legs & Paws	☐ Good	☐	Range, Cracked Pads or Broken Nails
9	Back Legs & Paws	☐ Good	☐	Range, Cracked Pads or Broken Nails
10	Abdomen	☐ Good	☐	Rigid, Pain/Odor Discharge Pain
	Genitals / Glands	☐ Good	☐	Rigid, Pain/Odor Discharge Pain
	Anal Area	☐ Good	☐	Hair, Debris or Feces
11	Skin & Coat	☐ Good	☐	Dry, Hairloss, Hot Spots or Bumps
12	Tail	☐ Good	☐	Deformity, Range of Use

SNOUT-TO-TAIL™ WORKSHEET

Date	Weight	Coat Color
Pulse	Temp	Breathing

Notes / Describe Issues

Photo Here

#	Area		Good		Issue
1	Snout & Muzzle	☐	Good	☐	Dry, Cracked or Discharge
2	Gums & Teeth	☐	Good	☐	Discoloration, Odor or Tartar
3	Eyes	☐	Good	☐	Clear, Hazy or Discharge
	Whites of Eyes	☐	White	☐ Red	☐ Yellow
4	Skull	☐	Good	☐	Bumps, Lumps or Pain/Sensitivity
5	Ears	☐	Good	☐	Odor, Discharge or Sensitive
6	Neck & Spine	☐	Good	☐	Lumps, Sores or Pain/Sensitivity
7	Chest & Ribs	☐	Good	☐	Lumps, Sores or Pain/Sensitivity
8	Front Legs & Paws	☐	Good	☐	Range, Cracked Pads or Broken Nails
9	Back Legs & Paws	☐	Good	☐	Range, Cracked Pads or Broken Nails
10	Abdomen	☐	Good	☐	Rigid, Pain/Odor Discharge Pain
	Genitals / Glands	☐	Good	☐	Rigid, Pain/Odor Discharge Pain
	Anal Area	☐	Good	☐	Hair, Debris or Feces
11	Skin & Coat	☐	Good	☐	Dry, Hairloss, Hot Spots or Bumps
12	Tail	☐	Good	☐	Deformity, Range of Use

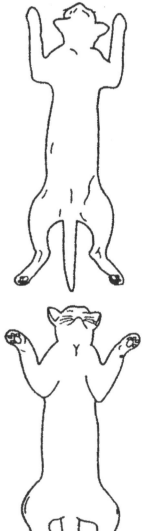

Indicate issue area(s).

SNOUT-TO-TAIL™ WORKSHEET

Date	Weight	Coat Color
Pulse	Temp	Breathing

Notes / Describe Issues

Photo Here

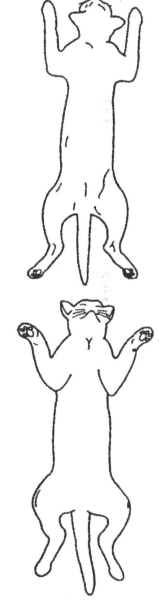

#	Area	Good	Issue
1	Snout & Muzzle	Good	Dry, Cracked or Discharge
2	Gums & Teeth	Good	Discoloration, Odor or Tartar
3	Eyes	Good	Clear, Hazy or Discharge
	Whites of Eyes	White	Red Yellow
4	Skull	Good	Bumps, Lumps or Pain/Sensitivity
5	Ears	Good	Odor, Discharge or Sensitive
6	Neck & Spine	Good	Lumps, Sores or Pain/Sensitivity
7	Chest & Ribs	Good	Lumps, Sores or Pain/Sensitivity
8	Front Legs & Paws	Good	Range, Cracked Pads or Broken Nails
9	Back Legs & Paws	Good	Range, Cracked Pads or Broken Nails
10	Abdomen	Good	Rigid, Pain/Odor Discharge Pain
	Genitals / Glands	Good	Rigid, Pain/Odor Discharge Pain
	Anal Area	Good	Hair, Debris or Feces
11	Skin & Coat	Good	Dry, Hairloss, Hot Spots or Bumps
12	Tail	Good	Deformity, Range of Use

SNOUT-TO-TAIL™ WORKSHEET

Date	Weight	Coat Color
Pulse	Temp	Breathing

Notes / Describe Issues

Photo Here

1	Snout & Muzzle	☐ Good	☐ Dry, Cracked or Discharge		
2	Gums & Teeth	☐ Good	☐ Discoloration, Odor or Tartar		
3	Eyes	☐ Good	☐ Clear, Hazy or Discharge		
	Whites of Eyes	☐ White	☐ Red	☐ Yellow	
4	Skull	☐ Good	☐ Bumps, Lumps or Pain/Sensitivity		
5	Ears	☐ Good	☐ Odor, Discharge or Sensitive		
6	Neck & Spine	☐ Good	☐ Lumps, Sores or Pain/Sensitivity		
7	Chest & Ribs	☐ Good	☐ Lumps, Sores or Pain/Sensitivity		
8	Front Legs & Paws	☐ Good	☐ Range, Cracked Pads or Broken Nails		
9	Back Legs & Paws	☐ Good	☐ Range, Cracked Pads or Broken Nails		
10	Abdomen	☐ Good	☐ Rigid, Pain/Odor Discharge Pain		
	Genitals / Glands	☐ Good	☐ Rigid, Pain/Odor Discharge Pain		
	Anal Area	☐ Good	☐ Hair, Debris or Feces		
11	Skin & Coat	☐ Good	☐ Dry, Hairloss, Hot Spots or Bumps		
12	Tail	☐ Good	☐ Deformity, Range of Use		

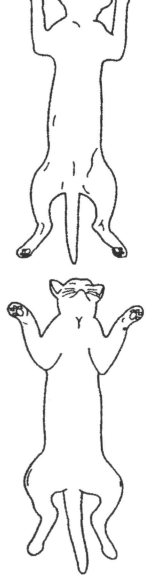

Indicate issue area(s).

SNOUT-TO-TAIL™ WORKSHEET

Date	Weight	Coat Color
Pulse	Temp	Breathing

Notes / Describe Issues

Photo Here

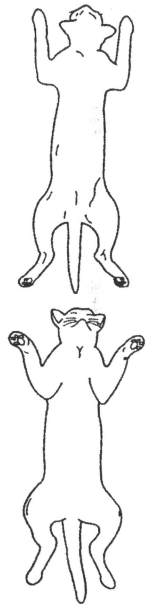

1	Snout & Muzzle	Good	Dry, Cracked or Discharge
2	Gums & Teeth	Good	Discoloration, Odor or Tartar
3	Eyes	Good	Clear, Hazy or Discharge
	Whites of Eyes	White	Red Yellow
4	Skull	Good	Bumps, Lumps or Pain/Sensitivity
5	Ears	Good	Odor, Discharge or Sensitive
6	Neck & Spine	Good	Lumps, Sores or Pain/Sensitivity
7	Chest & Ribs	Good	Lumps, Sores or Pain/Sensitivity
8	Front Legs & Paws	Good	Range, Cracked Pads or Broken Nails
9	Back Legs & Paws	Good	Range, Cracked Pads or Broken Nails
10	Abdomen	Good	Rigid, Pain/Odor Discharge Pain
	Genitals / Glands	Good	Rigid, Pain/Odor Discharge Pain
	Anal Area	Good	Hair, Debris or Feces
11	Skin & Coat	Good	Dry, Hairloss, Hot Spots or Bumps
12	Tail	Good	Deformity, Range of Use

SNOUT-TO-TAIL™ WORKSHEET

Date	Weight	Coat Color
Pulse	Temp	Breathing

Notes / Describe Issues

Photo Here

1	Snout & Muzzle	☐ Good	☐ Dry, Cracked or Discharge		
2	Gums & Teeth	☐ Good	☐ Discoloration, Odor or Tartar		
3	Eyes	☐ Good	☐ Clear, Hazy or Discharge		
	Whites of Eyes	☐ White	☐ Red	☐ Yellow	
4	Skull	☐ Good	☐ Bumps, Lumps or Pain/Sensitivity		
5	Ears	☐ Good	☐ Odor, Discharge or Sensitive		
6	Neck & Spine	☐ Good	☐ Lumps, Sores or Pain/Sensitivity		
7	Chest & Ribs	☐ Good	☐ Lumps, Sores or Pain/Sensitivity		
8	Front Legs & Paws	☐ Good	☐ Range, Cracked Pads or Broken Nails		
9	Back Legs & Paws	☐ Good	☐ Range, Cracked Pads or Broken Nails		
10	Abdomen	☐ Good	☐ Rigid, Pain/Odor Discharge Pain		
	Genitals / Glands	☐ Good	☐ Rigid, Pain/Odor Discharge Pain		
	Anal Area	☐ Good	☐ Hair, Debris or Feces		
11	Skin & Coat	☐ Good	☐ Dry, Hairloss, Hot Spots or Bumps		
12	Tail	☐ Good	☐ Deformity, Range of Use		

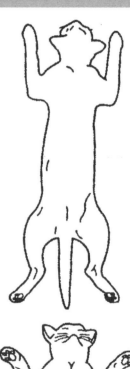

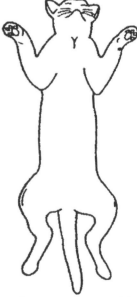

Indicate issue area(s).

SNOUT-TO-TAIL™ WORKSHEET

Date	Weight	Coat Color
Pulse	Temp	Breathing

Notes / Describe Issues

Photo Here

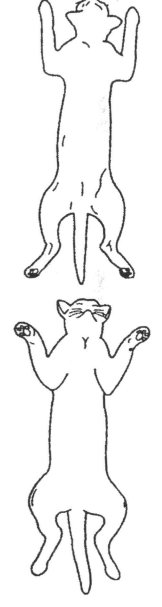

#	Area			
1	Snout & Muzzle	Good		Dry, Cracked or Discharge
2	Gums & Teeth	Good		Discoloration, Odor or Tartar
3	Eyes	Good		Clear, Hazy or Discharge
	Whites of Eyes	White	Red	Yellow
4	Skull	Good		Bumps, Lumps or Pain/Sensitivity
5	Ears	Good		Odor, Discharge or Sensitive
6	Neck & Spine	Good		Lumps, Sores or Pain/Sensitivity
7	Chest & Ribs	Good		Lumps, Sores or Pain/Sensitivity
8	Front Legs & Paws	Good		Range, Cracked Pads or Broken Nails
9	Back Legs & Paws	Good		Range, Cracked Pads or Broken Nails
10	Abdomen	Good		Rigid, Pain/Odor Discharge Pain
	Genitals / Glands	Good		Rigid, Pain/Odor Discharge Pain
	Anal Area	Good		Hair, Debris or Feces
11	Skin & Coat	Good		Dry, Hairloss, Hot Spots or Bumps
12	Tail	Good		Deformity, Range of Use

SNOUT-TO-TAIL™ WORKSHEET

Date	Weight	Coat Color
Pulse	Temp	Breathing

Notes / Describe Issues

Photo Here

1	Snout & Muzzle	☐ Good	☐ Dry, Cracked or Discharge	
2	Gums & Teeth	☐ Good	☐ Discoloration, Odor or Tartar	
3	Eyes	☐ Good	☐ Clear, Hazy or Discharge	
	Whites of Eyes	☐ White	☐ Red	☐ Yellow
4	Skull	☐ Good	☐ Bumps, Lumps or Pain/Sensitivity	
5	Ears	☐ Good	☐ Odor, Discharge or Sensitive	
6	Neck & Spine	☐ Good	☐ Lumps, Sores or Pain/Sensitivity	
7	Chest & Ribs	☐ Good	☐ Lumps, Sores or Pain/Sensitivity	
8	Front Legs & Paws	☐ Good	☐ Range, Cracked Pads or Broken Nails	
9	Back Legs & Paws	☐ Good	☐ Range, Cracked Pads or Broken Nails	
10	Abdomen	☐ Good	☐ Rigid, Pain/Odor Discharge Pain	
	Genitals / Glands	☐ Good	☐ Rigid, Pain/Odor Discharge Pain	
	Anal Area	☐ Good	☐ Hair, Debris or Feces	
11	Skin & Coat	☐ Good	☐ Dry, Hairloss, Hot Spots or Bumps	
12	Tail	☐ Good	☐ Deformity, Range of Use	

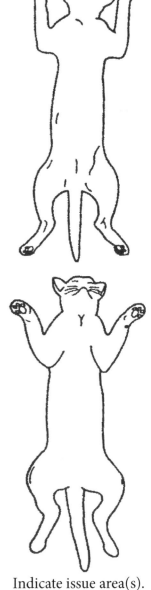

Indicate issue area(s).

SNOUT-TO-TAIL™ WORKSHEET

Date	Weight	Coat Color
Pulse	Temp	Breathing

Notes / Describe Issues

Photo Here

1	Snout & Muzzle	☐ Good	☐ Dry, Cracked or Discharge
2	Gums & Teeth	☐ Good	☐ Discoloration, Odor or Tartar
3	Eyes	☐ Good	☐ Clear, Hazy or Discharge
	Whites of Eyes	☐ White	☐ Red ☐ Yellow
4	Skull	☐ Good	☐ Bumps, Lumps or Pain/Sensitivity
5	Ears	☐ Good	☐ Odor, Discharge or Sensitive
6	Neck & Spine	☐ Good	☐ Lumps, Sores or Pain/Sensitivity
7	Chest & Ribs	☐ Good	☐ Lumps, Sores or Pain/Sensitivity
8	Front Legs & Paws	☐ Good	☐ Range, Cracked Pads or Broken Nails
9	Back Legs & Paws	☐ Good	☐ Range, Cracked Pads or Broken Nails
10	Abdomen	☐ Good	☐ Rigid, Pain/Odor Discharge Pain
	Genitals / Glands	☐ Good	☐ Rigid, Pain/Odor Discharge Pain
	Anal Area	☐ Good	☐ Hair, Debris or Feces
11	Skin & Coat	☐ Good	☐ Dry, Hairloss, Hot Spots or Bumps
12	Tail	☐ Good	☐ Deformity, Range of Use

SNOUT-TO-TAIL™ WORKSHEET

Date	Weight	Coat Color
Pulse	Temp	Breathing

Notes / Describe Issues

Photo Here

1	Snout & Muzzle	Good	Dry, Cracked or Discharge
2	Gums & Teeth	Good	Discoloration, Odor or Tartar
3	Eyes	Good	Clear, Hazy or Discharge
	Whites of Eyes	White	Red	Yellow
4	Skull	Good	Bumps, Lumps or Pain/Sensitivity
5	Ears	Good	Odor, Discharge or Sensitive
6	Neck & Spine	Good	Lumps, Sores or Pain/Sensitivity
7	Chest & Ribs	Good	Lumps, Sores or Pain/Sensitivity
8	Front Legs & Paws	Good	Range, Cracked Pads or Broken Nails
9	Back Legs & Paws	Good	Range, Cracked Pads or Broken Nails
10	Abdomen	Good	Rigid, Pain/Odor Discharge Pain
	Genitals / Glands	Good	Rigid, Pain/Odor Discharge Pain
	Anal Area	Good	Hair, Debris or Feces
11	Skin & Coat	Good	Dry, Hairloss, Hot Spots or Bumps
12	Tail	Good	Deformity, Range of Use

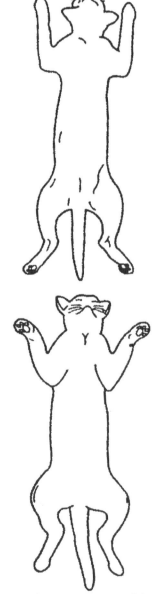

Indicate issue area(s).

SNOUT-TO-TAIL™ WORKSHEET

Date	Weight	Coat Color
Pulse	Temp	Breathing

Notes / Describe Issues

Photo Here

1	Snout & Muzzle	☐ Good	☐ Dry, Cracked or Discharge		
2	Gums & Teeth	☐ Good	☐ Discoloration, Odor or Tartar		
3	Eyes	☐ Good	☐ Clear, Hazy or Discharge		
	Whites of Eyes	☐ White	☐ Red	☐ Yellow	
4	Skull	☐ Good	☐ Bumps, Lumps or Pain/Sensitivity		
5	Ears	☐ Good	☐ Odor, Discharge or Sensitive		
6	Neck & Spine	☐ Good	☐ Lumps, Sores or Pain/Sensitivity		
7	Chest & Ribs	☐ Good	☐ Lumps, Sores or Pain/Sensitivity		
8	Front Legs & Paws	☐ Good	☐ Range, Cracked Pads or Broken Nails		
9	Back Legs & Paws	☐ Good	☐ Range, Cracked Pads or Broken Nails		
10	Abdomen	☐ Good	☐ Rigid, Pain/Odor Discharge Pain		
	Genitals / Glands	☐ Good	☐ Rigid, Pain/Odor Discharge Pain		
	Anal Area	☐ Good	☐ Hair, Debris or Feces		
11	Skin & Coat	☐ Good	☐ Dry, Hairloss, Hot Spots or Bumps		
12	Tail	☐ Good	☐ Deformity, Range of Use		

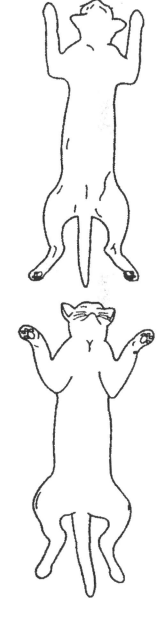

SNOUT-TO-TAIL™ WORKSHEET

Date	Weight	Coat Color
Pulse	Temp	Breathing

Notes / Describe Issues

Photo Here

#		Good		
1	Snout & Muzzle	☐ Good	☐ Dry, Cracked or Discharge	
2	Gums & Teeth	☐ Good	☐ Discoloration, Odor or Tartar	
3	Eyes	☐ Good	☐ Clear, Hazy or Discharge	
	Whites of Eyes	☐ White	☐ Red	☐ Yellow
4	Skull	☐ Good	☐ Bumps, Lumps or Pain/Sensitivity	
5	Ears	☐ Good	☐ Odor, Discharge or Sensitive	
6	Neck & Spine	☐ Good	☐ Lumps, Sores or Pain/Sensitivity	
7	Chest & Ribs	☐ Good	☐ Lumps, Sores or Pain/Sensitivity	
8	Front Legs & Paws	☐ Good	☐ Range, Cracked Pads or Broken Nails	
9	Back Legs & Paws	☐ Good	☐ Range, Cracked Pads or Broken Nails	
10	Abdomen	☐ Good	☐ Rigid, Pain/Odor Discharge Pain	
	Genitals / Glands	☐ Good	☐ Rigid, Pain/Odor Discharge Pain	
	Anal Area	☐ Good	☐ Hair, Debris or Feces	
11	Skin & Coat	☐ Good	☐ Dry, Hairloss, Hot Spots or Bumps	
12	Tail	☐ Good	☐ Deformity, Range of Use	

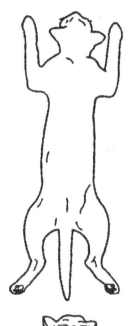

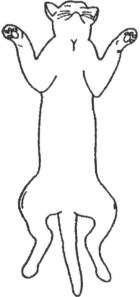

Indicate issue area(s).

SNOUT-TO-TAIL™ WORKSHEET

Date	Weight	Coat Color
Pulse	Temp	Breathing

Notes / Describe Issues

Photo Here

1	Snout & Muzzle		Good		Dry, Cracked or Discharge	
2	Gums & Teeth		Good		Discoloration, Odor or Tartar	
3	Eyes		Good		Clear, Hazy or Discharge	
	Whites of Eyes		White	Red	Yellow	
4	Skull		Good		Bumps, Lumps or Pain/Sensitivity	
5	Ears		Good		Odor, Discharge or Sensitive	
6	Neck & Spine		Good		Lumps, Sores or Pain/Sensitivity	
7	Chest & Ribs		Good		Lumps, Sores or Pain/Sensitivity	
8	Front Legs & Paws		Good		Range, Cracked Pads or Broken Nails	
9	Back Legs & Paws		Good		Range, Cracked Pads or Broken Nails	
10	Abdomen		Good		Rigid, Pain/Odor Discharge Pain	
	Genitals / Glands		Good		Rigid, Pain/Odor Discharge Pain	
	Anal Area		Good		Hair, Debris or Feces	
11	Skin & Coat		Good		Dry, Hairloss, Hot Spots or Bumps	
12	Tail		Good		Deformity, Range of Use	

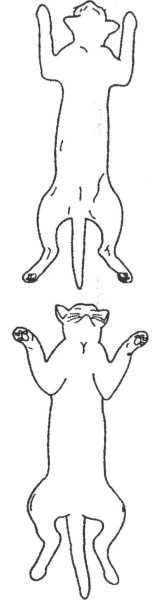

SNOUT-TO-TAIL™ WORKSHEET

Date	Weight	Coat Color
Pulse	Temp	Breathing

Notes / Describe Issues

Photo Here

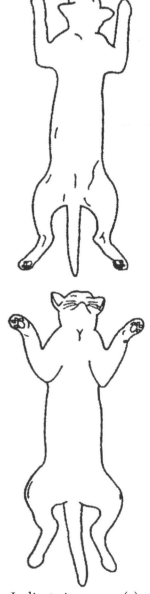

1	Snout & Muzzle	☐ Good		Dry, Cracked or Discharge	
2	Gums & Teeth	☐ Good		Discoloration, Odor or Tartar	
3	Eyes	☐ Good		Clear, Hazy or Discharge	
	Whites of Eyes	☐ White	☐ Red	☐ Yellow	
4	Skull	☐ Good		Bumps, Lumps or Pain/Sensitivity	
5	Ears	☐ Good		Odor, Discharge or Sensitive	
6	Neck & Spine	☐ Good		Lumps, Sores or Pain/Sensitivity	
7	Chest & Ribs	☐ Good		Lumps, Sores or Pain/Sensitivity	
8	Front Legs & Paws	☐ Good		Range, Cracked Pads or Broken Nails	
9	Back Legs & Paws	☐ Good		Range, Cracked Pads or Broken Nails	
10	Abdomen	☐ Good		Rigid, Pain/Odor Discharge Pain	
	Genitals / Glands	☐ Good		Rigid, Pain/Odor Discharge Pain	
	Anal Area	☐ Good		Hair, Debris or Feces	
11	Skin & Coat	☐ Good		Dry, Hairloss, Hot Spots or Bumps	
12	Tail	☐ Good		Deformity, Range of Use	

Indicate issue area(s).

SNOUT-TO-TAIL™ WORKSHEET

Date	Weight	Coat Color
Pulse	Temp	Breathing

Notes / Describe Issues

Photo Here

1	Snout & Muzzle	Good		Dry, Cracked or Discharge
2	Gums & Teeth	Good		Discoloration, Odor or Tartar
3	Eyes	Good		Clear, Hazy or Discharge
	Whites of Eyes	White	Red	Yellow
4	Skull	Good		Bumps, Lumps or Pain/Sensitivity
5	Ears	Good		Odor, Discharge or Sensitive
6	Neck & Spine	Good		Lumps, Sores or Pain/Sensitivity
7	Chest & Ribs	Good		Lumps, Sores or Pain/Sensitivity
8	Front Legs & Paws	Good		Range, Cracked Pads or Broken Nails
9	Back Legs & Paws	Good		Range, Cracked Pads or Broken Nails
10	Abdomen	Good		Rigid, Pain/Odor Discharge Pain
	Genitals / Glands	Good		Rigid, Pain/Odor Discharge Pain
	Anal Area	Good		Hair, Debris or Feces
11	Skin & Coat	Good		Dry, Hairloss, Hot Spots or Bumps
12	Tail	Good		Deformity, Range of Use

SNOUT-TO-TAIL™ WORKSHEET

Date	Weight	Coat Color
Pulse	Temp	Breathing

Notes / Describe Issues

Photo Here

#		Good	
1	Snout & Muzzle	☐ Good	☐ Dry, Cracked or Discharge
2	Gums & Teeth	☐ Good	☐ Discoloration, Odor or Tartar
3	Eyes	☐ Good	☐ Clear, Hazy or Discharge
	Whites of Eyes	☐ White	☐ Red ☐ Yellow
4	Skull	☐ Good	☐ Bumps, Lumps or Pain/Sensitivity
5	Ears	☐ Good	☐ Odor, Discharge or Sensitive
6	Neck & Spine	☐ Good	☐ Lumps, Sores or Pain/Sensitivity
7	Chest & Ribs	☐ Good	☐ Lumps, Sores or Pain/Sensitivity
8	Front Legs & Paws	☐ Good	☐ Range, Cracked Pads or Broken Nails
9	Back Legs & Paws	☐ Good	☐ Range, Cracked Pads or Broken Nails
10	Abdomen	☐ Good	☐ Rigid, Pain/Odor Discharge Pain
	Genitals / Glands	☐ Good	☐ Rigid, Pain/Odor Discharge Pain
	Anal Area	☐ Good	☐ Hair, Debris or Feces
11	Skin & Coat	☐ Good	☐ Dry, Hairloss, Hot Spots or Bumps
12	Tail	☐ Good	☐ Deformity, Range of Use

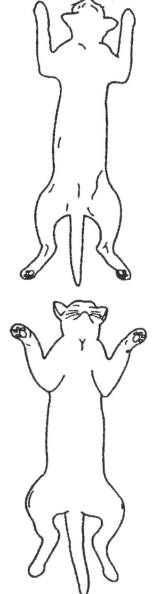

Indicate issue area(s).

SNOUT-TO-TAIL™ WORKSHEET

Date	Weight	Coat Color
Pulse	Temp	Breathing

Notes / Describe Issues

Photo Here

1	Snout & Muzzle	☐ Good		☐ Dry, Cracked or Discharge	
2	Gums & Teeth	☐ Good		☐ Discoloration, Odor or Tartar	
3	Eyes	☐ Good		☐ Clear, Hazy or Discharge	
	Whites of Eyes	☐ White	☐ Red	☐ Yellow	
4	Skull	☐ Good		☐ Bumps, Lumps or Pain/Sensitivity	
5	Ears	☐ Good		☐ Odor, Discharge or Sensitive	
6	Neck & Spine	☐ Good		☐ Lumps, Sores or Pain/Sensitivity	
7	Chest & Ribs	☐ Good		☐ Lumps, Sores or Pain/Sensitivity	
8	Front Legs & Paws	☐ Good		☐ Range, Cracked Pads or Broken Nails	
9	Back Legs & Paws	☐ Good		☐ Range, Cracked Pads or Broken Nails	
10	Abdomen	☐ Good		☐ Rigid, Pain/Odor Discharge Pain	
	Genitals / Glands	☐ Good		☐ Rigid, Pain/Odor Discharge Pain	
	Anal Area	☐ Good		☐ Hair, Debris or Feces	
11	Skin & Coat	☐ Good		☐ Dry, Hairloss, Hot Spots or Bumps	
12	Tail	☐ Good		☐ Deformity, Range of Use	

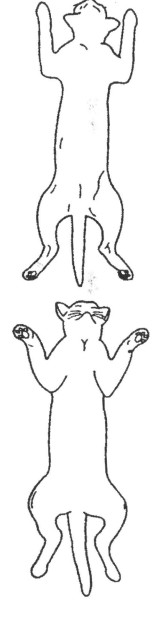

SNOUT-TO-TAIL™ WORKSHEET

Date	Weight	Coat Color
Pulse	Temp	Breathing

Notes / Describe Issues

Photo Here

#		Good	Issue
1	Snout & Muzzle	Good	Dry, Cracked or Discharge
2	Gums & Teeth	Good	Discoloration, Odor or Tartar
3	Eyes	Good	Clear, Hazy or Discharge
	Whites of Eyes	White	Red Yellow
4	Skull	Good	Bumps, Lumps or Pain/Sensitivity
5	Ears	Good	Odor, Discharge or Sensitive
6	Neck & Spine	Good	Lumps, Sores or Pain/Sensitivity
7	Chest & Ribs	Good	Lumps, Sores or Pain/Sensitivity
8	Front Legs & Paws	Good	Range, Cracked Pads or Broken Nails
9	Back Legs & Paws	Good	Range, Cracked Pads or Broken Nails
10	Abdomen	Good	Rigid, Pain/Odor Discharge Pain
	Genitals / Glands	Good	Rigid, Pain/Odor Discharge Pain
	Anal Area	Good	Hair, Debris or Feces
11	Skin & Coat	Good	Dry, Hairloss, Hot Spots or Bumps
12	Tail	Good	Deformity, Range of Use

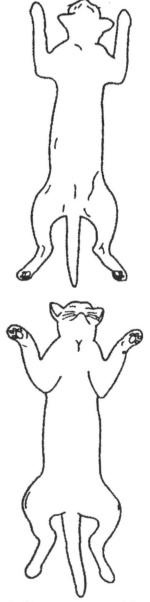

Indicate issue area(s).

SNOUT-TO-TAIL™ WORKSHEET

Date	Weight	Coat Color
Pulse	Temp	Breathing

Notes / Describe Issues

Photo Here

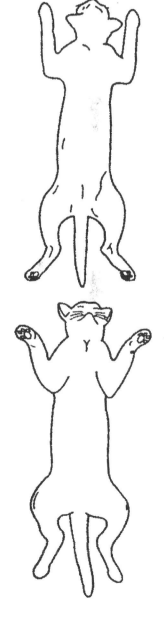

1	Snout & Muzzle	Good	Dry, Cracked or Discharge
2	Gums & Teeth	Good	Discoloration, Odor or Tartar
3	Eyes	Good	Clear, Hazy or Discharge
	Whites of Eyes	White	Red	Yellow
4	Skull	Good	Bumps, Lumps or Pain/Sensitivity
5	Ears	Good	Odor, Discharge or Sensitive
6	Neck & Spine	Good	Lumps, Sores or Pain/Sensitivity
7	Chest & Ribs	Good	Lumps, Sores or Pain/Sensitivity
8	Front Legs & Paws	Good	Range, Cracked Pads or Broken Nails
9	Back Legs & Paws	Good	Range, Cracked Pads or Broken Nails
10	Abdomen	Good	Rigid, Pain/Odor Discharge Pain
	Genitals / Glands	Good	Rigid, Pain/Odor Discharge Pain
	Anal Area	Good	Hair, Debris or Feces
11	Skin & Coat	Good	Dry, Hairloss, Hot Spots or Bumps
12	Tail	Good	Deformity, Range of Use

SNOUT-TO-TAIL™ WORKSHEET

Date	Weight	Coat Color
Pulse	Temp	Breathing

Notes / Describe Issues

Photo Here

#	Area		Good		Issue
1	Snout & Muzzle		Good		Dry, Cracked or Discharge
2	Gums & Teeth		Good		Discoloration, Odor or Tartar
3	Eyes		Good		Clear, Hazy or Discharge
	Whites of Eyes		White	Red	Yellow
4	Skull		Good		Bumps, Lumps or Pain/Sensitivity
5	Ears		Good		Odor, Discharge or Sensitive
6	Neck & Spine		Good		Lumps, Sores or Pain/Sensitivity
7	Chest & Ribs		Good		Lumps, Sores or Pain/Sensitivity
8	Front Legs & Paws		Good		Range, Cracked Pads or Broken Nails
9	Back Legs & Paws		Good		Range, Cracked Pads or Broken Nails
10	Abdomen		Good		Rigid, Pain/Odor Discharge Pain
	Genitals / Glands		Good		Rigid, Pain/Odor Discharge Pain
	Anal Area		Good		Hair, Debris or Feces
11	Skin & Coat		Good		Dry, Hairloss, Hot Spots or Bumps
12	Tail		Good		Deformity, Range of Use

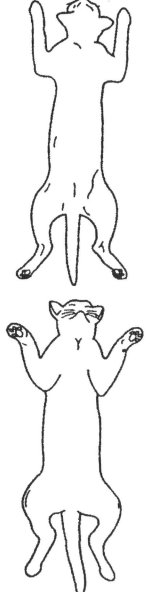

Indicate issue area(s).

SNOUT-TO-TAIL™ WORKSHEET

Date	Weight	Coat Color
Pulse	Temp	Breathing

Notes / Describe Issues

Photo Here

1 Snout & Muzzle ☐ Good ☐ Dry, Cracked or Discharge

2 Gums & Teeth ☐ Good ☐ Discoloration, Odor or Tartar

3 Eyes ☐ Good ☐ Clear, Hazy or Discharge

Whites of Eyes ☐ White ☐ Red ☐ Yellow

4 Skull ☐ Good ☐ Bumps, Lumps or Pain/Sensitivity

5 Ears ☐ Good ☐ Odor, Discharge or Sensitive

6 Neck & Spine ☐ Good ☐ Lumps, Sores or Pain/Sensitivity

7 Chest & Ribs ☐ Good ☐ Lumps, Sores or Pain/Sensitivity

8 Front Legs & Paws ☐ Good ☐ Range, Cracked Pads or Broken Nails

9 Back Legs & Paws ☐ Good ☐ Range, Cracked Pads or Broken Nails

10 Abdomen ☐ Good ☐ Rigid, Pain/Odor Discharge Pain

Genitals / Glands ☐ Good ☐ Rigid, Pain/Odor Discharge Pain

Anal Area ☐ Good ☐ Hair, Debris or Feces

11 Skin & Coat ☐ Good ☐ Dry, Hairloss, Hot Spots or Bumps

12 Tail ☐ Good ☐ Deformity, Range of Use

SNOUT-TO-TAIL™ WORKSHEET

Date	Weight	Coat Color
Pulse	Temp	Breathing

Notes / Describe Issues

Photo Here

1	Snout & Muzzle	Good	Dry, Cracked or Discharge
2	Gums & Teeth	Good	Discoloration, Odor or Tartar
3	Eyes	Good	Clear, Hazy or Discharge
	Whites of Eyes	White	Red	Yellow
4	Skull	Good	Bumps, Lumps or Pain/Sensitivity
5	Ears	Good	Odor, Discharge or Sensitive
6	Neck & Spine	Good	Lumps, Sores or Pain/Sensitivity
7	Chest & Ribs	Good	Lumps, Sores or Pain/Sensitivity
8	Front Legs & Paws	Good	Range, Cracked Pads or Broken Nails
9	Back Legs & Paws	Good	Range, Cracked Pads or Broken Nails
10	Abdomen	Good	Rigid, Pain/Odor Discharge Pain
	Genitals / Glands	Good	Rigid, Pain/Odor Discharge Pain
	Anal Area	Good	Hair, Debris or Feces
11	Skin & Coat	Good	Dry, Hairloss, Hot Spots or Bumps
12	Tail	Good	Deformity, Range of Use

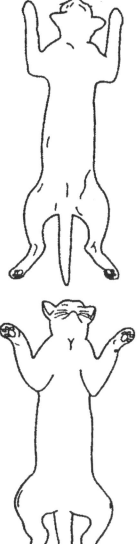

Indicate issue area(s).

SNOUT-TO-TAIL™ WORKSHEET

Date	Weight	Coat Color
Pulse	Temp	Breathing

Notes / Describe Issues

Photo Here

#	Area	Good	Issue
1	Snout & Muzzle	Good	Dry, Cracked or Discharge
2	Gums & Teeth	Good	Discoloration, Odor or Tartar
3	Eyes	Good	Clear, Hazy or Discharge
	Whites of Eyes	White	Red / Yellow
4	Skull	Good	Bumps, Lumps or Pain/Sensitivity
5	Ears	Good	Odor, Discharge or Sensitive
6	Neck & Spine	Good	Lumps, Sores or Pain/Sensitivity
7	Chest & Ribs	Good	Lumps, Sores or Pain/Sensitivity
8	Front Legs & Paws	Good	Range, Cracked Pads or Broken Nails
9	Back Legs & Paws	Good	Range, Cracked Pads or Broken Nails
10	Abdomen	Good	Rigid, Pain/Odor Discharge Pain
	Genitals / Glands	Good	Rigid, Pain/Odor Discharge Pain
	Anal Area	Good	Hair, Debris or Feces
11	Skin & Coat	Good	Dry, Hairloss, Hot Spots or Bumps
12	Tail	Good	Deformity, Range of Use

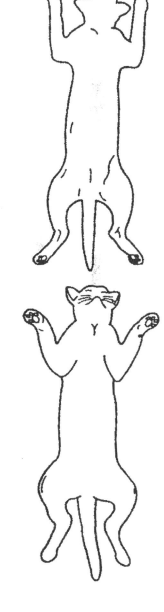

SNOUT-TO-TAIL™ WORKSHEET

Date	Weight	Coat Color
Pulse	Temp	Breathing

Notes / Describe Issues

Photo Here

#		Good	Issue
1	Snout & Muzzle	☐ Good	☐ Dry, Cracked or Discharge
2	Gums & Teeth	☐ Good	☐ Discoloration, Odor or Tartar
3	Eyes	☐ Good	☐ Clear, Hazy or Discharge
	Whites of Eyes	☐ White	☐ Red ☐ Yellow
4	Skull	☐ Good	☐ Bumps, Lumps or Pain/Sensitivity
5	Ears	☐ Good	☐ Odor, Discharge or Sensitive
6	Neck & Spine	☐ Good	☐ Lumps, Sores or Pain/Sensitivity
7	Chest & Ribs	☐ Good	☐ Lumps, Sores or Pain/Sensitivity
8	Front Legs & Paws	☐ Good	☐ Range, Cracked Pads or Broken Nails
9	Back Legs & Paws	☐ Good	☐ Range, Cracked Pads or Broken Nails
10	Abdomen	☐ Good	☐ Rigid, Pain/Odor Discharge Pain
	Genitals / Glands	☐ Good	☐ Rigid, Pain/Odor Discharge Pain
	Anal Area	☐ Good	☐ Hair, Debris or Feces
11	Skin & Coat	☐ Good	☐ Dry, Hairloss, Hot Spots or Bumps
12	Tail	☐ Good	☐ Deformity, Range of Use

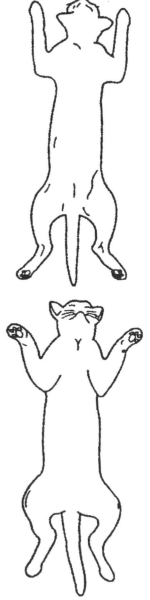

Indicate issue area(s).

SNOUT-TO-TAIL™ WORKSHEET

Date	Weight	Coat Color
Pulse	Temp	Breathing

Notes / Describe Issues

Photo Here

#	Area	Good	Issue
1	Snout & Muzzle	Good	Dry, Cracked or Discharge
2	Gums & Teeth	Good	Discoloration, Odor or Tartar
3	Eyes	Good	Clear, Hazy or Discharge
	Whites of Eyes	White	Red / Yellow
4	Skull	Good	Bumps, Lumps or Pain/Sensitivity
5	Ears	Good	Odor, Discharge or Sensitive
6	Neck & Spine	Good	Lumps, Sores or Pain/Sensitivity
7	Chest & Ribs	Good	Lumps, Sores or Pain/Sensitivity
8	Front Legs & Paws	Good	Range, Cracked Pads or Broken Nails
9	Back Legs & Paws	Good	Range, Cracked Pads or Broken Nails
10	Abdomen	Good	Rigid, Pain/Odor Discharge Pain
	Genitals / Glands	Good	Rigid, Pain/Odor Discharge Pain
	Anal Area	Good	Hair, Debris or Feces
11	Skin & Coat	Good	Dry, Hairloss, Hot Spots or Bumps
12	Tail	Good	Deformity, Range of Use

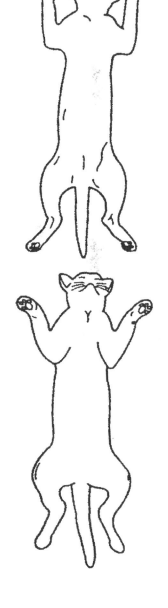

SNOUT-TO-TAIL™ WORKSHEET

Date	Weight	Coat Color
Pulse	Temp	Breathing

Notes / Describe Issues

Photo Here

#	Area			
1	Snout & Muzzle	☐ Good	☐ Dry, Cracked or Discharge	
2	Gums & Teeth	☐ Good	☐ Discoloration, Odor or Tartar	
3	Eyes	☐ Good	☐ Clear, Hazy or Discharge	
	Whites of Eyes	☐ White	☐ Red	☐ Yellow
4	Skull	☐ Good	☐ Bumps, Lumps or Pain/Sensitivity	
5	Ears	☐ Good	☐ Odor, Discharge or Sensitive	
6	Neck & Spine	☐ Good	☐ Lumps, Sores or Pain/Sensitivity	
7	Chest & Ribs	☐ Good	☐ Lumps, Sores or Pain/Sensitivity	
8	Front Legs & Paws	☐ Good	☐ Range, Cracked Pads or Broken Nails	
9	Back Legs & Paws	☐ Good	☐ Range, Cracked Pads or Broken Nails	
10	Abdomen	☐ Good	☐ Rigid, Pain/Odor Discharge Pain	
	Genitals / Glands	☐ Good	☐ Rigid, Pain/Odor Discharge Pain	
	Anal Area	☐ Good	☐ Hair, Debris or Feces	
11	Skin & Coat	☐ Good	☐ Dry, Hairloss, Hot Spots or Bumps	
12	Tail	☐ Good	☐ Deformity, Range of Use	

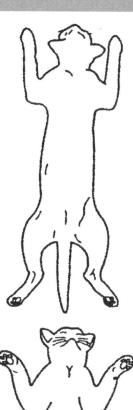

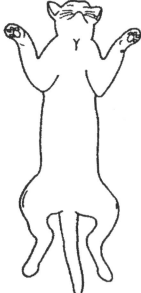

Indicate issue area(s).

SNOUT-TO-TAIL™ WORKSHEET

Date	Weight	Coat Color
Pulse	Temp	Breathing

Notes / Describe Issues

Photo Here

1	Snout & Muzzle	☐ Good	☐ Dry, Cracked or Discharge
2	Gums & Teeth	☐ Good	☐ Discoloration, Odor or Tartar
3	Eyes	☐ Good	☐ Clear, Hazy or Discharge
	Whites of Eyes	☐ White	☐ Red ☐ Yellow
4	Skull	☐ Good	☐ Bumps, Lumps or Pain/Sensitivity
5	Ears	☐ Good	☐ Odor, Discharge or Sensitive
6	Neck & Spine	☐ Good	☐ Lumps, Sores or Pain/Sensitivity
7	Chest & Ribs	☐ Good	☐ Lumps, Sores or Pain/Sensitivity
8	Front Legs & Paws	☐ Good	☐ Range, Cracked Pads or Broken Nails
9	Back Legs & Paws	☐ Good	☐ Range, Cracked Pads or Broken Nails
10	Abdomen	☐ Good	☐ Rigid, Pain/Odor Discharge Pain
	Genitals / Glands	☐ Good	☐ Rigid, Pain/Odor Discharge Pain
	Anal Area	☐ Good	☐ Hair, Debris or Feces
11	Skin & Coat	☐ Good	☐ Dry, Hairloss, Hot Spots or Bumps
12	Tail	☐ Good	☐ Deformity, Range of Use

SNOUT-TO-TAIL™ WORKSHEET

Date	Weight	Coat Color
Pulse	Temp	Breathing

Notes / Describe Issues

Photo Here

#	Area	Good	Issue
1	Snout & Muzzle	☐ Good	☐ Dry, Cracked or Discharge
2	Gums & Teeth	☐ Good	☐ Discoloration, Odor or Tartar
3	Eyes	☐ Good	☐ Clear, Hazy or Discharge
	Whites of Eyes	☐ White	☐ Red ☐ Yellow
4	Skull	☐ Good	☐ Bumps, Lumps or Pain/Sensitivity
5	Ears	☐ Good	☐ Odor, Discharge or Sensitive
6	Neck & Spine	☐ Good	☐ Lumps, Sores or Pain/Sensitivity
7	Chest & Ribs	☐ Good	☐ Lumps, Sores or Pain/Sensitivity
8	Front Legs & Paws	☐ Good	☐ Range, Cracked Pads or Broken Nails
9	Back Legs & Paws	☐ Good	☐ Range, Cracked Pads or Broken Nails
10	Abdomen	☐ Good	☐ Rigid, Pain/Odor Discharge Pain
	Genitals / Glands	☐ Good	☐ Rigid, Pain/Odor Discharge Pain
	Anal Area	☐ Good	☐ Hair, Debris or Feces
11	Skin & Coat	☐ Good	☐ Dry, Hairloss, Hot Spots or Bumps
12	Tail	☐ Good	☐ Deformity, Range of Use

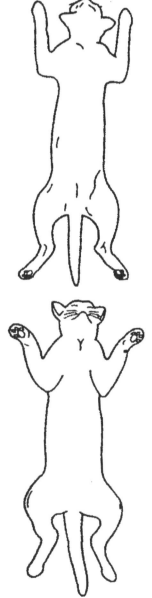

Indicate issue area(s).

SNOUT-TO-TAIL™ WORKSHEET

Date	Weight	Coat Color
Pulse	Temp	Breathing

Notes / Describe Issues

Photo Here

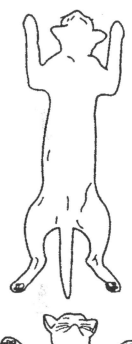

1	Snout & Muzzle	☐ Good		☐ Dry, Cracked or Discharge	
2	Gums & Teeth	☐ Good		☐ Discoloration, Odor or Tartar	
3	Eyes	☐ Good		☐ Clear, Hazy or Discharge	
	Whites of Eyes	☐ White	☐ Red	☐ Yellow	
4	Skull	☐ Good		☐ Bumps, Lumps or Pain/Sensitivity	
5	Ears	☐ Good		☐ Odor, Discharge or Sensitive	
6	Neck & Spine	☐ Good		☐ Lumps, Sores or Pain/Sensitivity	
7	Chest & Ribs	☐ Good		☐ Lumps, Sores or Pain/Sensitivity	
8	Front Legs & Paws	☐ Good		☐ Range, Cracked Pads or Broken Nails	
9	Back Legs & Paws	☐ Good		☐ Range, Cracked Pads or Broken Nails	
10	Abdomen	☐ Good		☐ Rigid, Pain/Odor Discharge Pain	
	Genitals / Glands	☐ Good		☐ Rigid, Pain/Odor Discharge Pain	
	Anal Area	☐ Good		☐ Hair, Debris or Feces	
11	Skin & Coat	☐ Good		☐ Dry, Hairloss, Hot Spots or Bumps	
12	Tail	☐ Good		☐ Deformity, Range of Use	

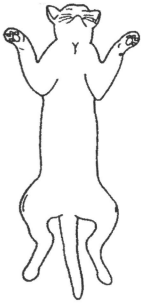

SNOUT-TO-TAIL™ WORKSHEET

Date	Weight	Coat Color
Pulse	Temp	Breathing

Notes / Describe Issues

Photo Here

1	Snout & Muzzle	☐ Good	☐ Dry, Cracked or Discharge
2	Gums & Teeth	☐ Good	☐ Discoloration, Odor or Tartar
3	Eyes	☐ Good	☐ Clear, Hazy or Discharge
	Whites of Eyes	☐ White	☐ Red ☐ Yellow
4	Skull	☐ Good	☐ Bumps, Lumps or Pain/Sensitivity
5	Ears	☐ Good	☐ Odor, Discharge or Sensitive
6	Neck & Spine	☐ Good	☐ Lumps, Sores or Pain/Sensitivity
7	Chest & Ribs	☐ Good	☐ Lumps, Sores or Pain/Sensitivity
8	Front Legs & Paws	☐ Good	☐ Range, Cracked Pads or Broken Nails
9	Back Legs & Paws	☐ Good	☐ Range, Cracked Pads or Broken Nails
10	Abdomen	☐ Good	☐ Rigid, Pain/Odor Discharge Pain
	Genitals / Glands	☐ Good	☐ Rigid, Pain/Odor Discharge Pain
	Anal Area	☐ Good	☐ Hair, Debris or Feces
11	Skin & Coat	☐ Good	☐ Dry, Hairloss, Hot Spots or Bumps
12	Tail	☐ Good	☐ Deformity, Range of Use

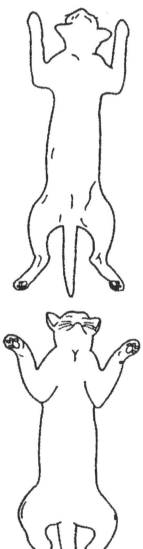

Indicate issue area(s).

SNOUT-TO-TAIL™ WORKSHEET

Date	Weight	Coat Color
Pulse	Temp	Breathing

Notes / Describe Issues

Photo Here

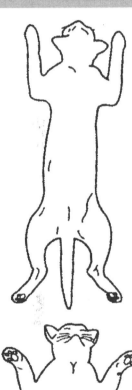

#	Area	Good	Issue
1	Snout & Muzzle	Good	Dry, Cracked or Discharge
2	Gums & Teeth	Good	Discoloration, Odor or Tartar
3	Eyes	Good	Clear, Hazy or Discharge
	Whites of Eyes	White	Red Yellow
4	Skull	Good	Bumps, Lumps or Pain/Sensitivity
5	Ears	Good	Odor, Discharge or Sensitive
6	Neck & Spine	Good	Lumps, Sores or Pain/Sensitivity
7	Chest & Ribs	Good	Lumps, Sores or Pain/Sensitivity
8	Front Legs & Paws	Good	Range, Cracked Pads or Broken Nails
9	Back Legs & Paws	Good	Range, Cracked Pads or Broken Nails
10	Abdomen	Good	Rigid, Pain/Odor Discharge Pain
	Genitals / Glands	Good	Rigid, Pain/Odor Discharge Pain
	Anal Area	Good	Hair, Debris or Feces
11	Skin & Coat	Good	Dry, Hairloss, Hot Spots or Bumps
12	Tail	Good	Deformity, Range of Use

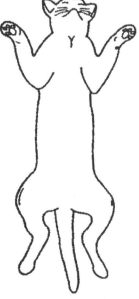

SNOUT-TO-TAIL™ WORKSHEET

Date	Weight	Coat Color
Pulse	Temp	Breathing

Notes / Describe Issues

Photo Here

1	Snout & Muzzle	☐ Good	☐ Dry, Cracked or Discharge		
2	Gums & Teeth	☐ Good	☐ Discoloration, Odor or Tartar		
3	Eyes	☐ Good	☐ Clear, Hazy or Discharge		
	Whites of Eyes	☐ White	☐ Red	☐ Yellow	
4	Skull	☐ Good	☐ Bumps, Lumps or Pain/Sensitivity		
5	Ears	☐ Good	☐ Odor, Discharge or Sensitive		
6	Neck & Spine	☐ Good	☐ Lumps, Sores or Pain/Sensitivity		
7	Chest & Ribs	☐ Good	☐ Lumps, Sores or Pain/Sensitivity		
8	Front Legs & Paws	☐ Good	☐ Range, Cracked Pads or Broken Nails		
9	Back Legs & Paws	☐ Good	☐ Range, Cracked Pads or Broken Nails		
10	Abdomen	☐ Good	☐ Rigid, Pain/Odor Discharge Pain		
	Genitals / Glands	☐ Good	☐ Rigid, Pain/Odor Discharge Pain		
	Anal Area	☐ Good	☐ Hair, Debris or Feces		
11	Skin & Coat	☐ Good	☐ Dry, Hairloss, Hot Spots or Bumps		
12	Tail	☐ Good	☐ Deformity, Range of Use		

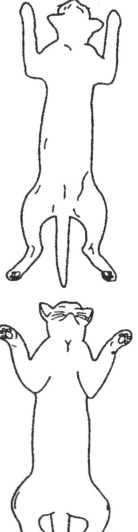

Indicate issue area(s).

SNOUT-TO-TAIL™ WORKSHEET

Date	Weight	Coat Color
Pulse	Temp	Breathing

Notes / Describe Issues

Photo Here

1	Snout & Muzzle	Good	Dry, Cracked or Discharge
2	Gums & Teeth	Good	Discoloration, Odor or Tartar
3	Eyes	Good	Clear, Hazy or Discharge
	Whites of Eyes	White	Red	Yellow
4	Skull	Good	Bumps, Lumps or Pain/Sensitivity
5	Ears	Good	Odor, Discharge or Sensitive
6	Neck & Spine	Good	Lumps, Sores or Pain/Sensitivity
7	Chest & Ribs	Good	Lumps, Sores or Pain/Sensitivity
8	Front Legs & Paws	Good	Range, Cracked Pads or Broken Nails
9	Back Legs & Paws	Good	Range, Cracked Pads or Broken Nails
10	Abdomen	Good	Rigid, Pain/Odor Discharge Pain
	Genitals / Glands	Good	Rigid, Pain/Odor Discharge Pain
	Anal Area	Good	Hair, Debris or Feces
11	Skin & Coat	Good	Dry, Hairloss, Hot Spots or Bumps
12	Tail	Good	Deformity, Range of Use

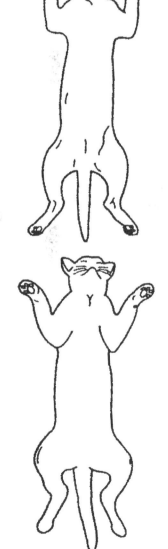

SNOUT-TO-TAIL™ WORKSHEET

Date	Weight	Coat Color
Pulse	Temp	Breathing

Notes / Describe Issues

Photo Here

1	Snout & Muzzle	☐ Good	☐	Dry, Cracked or Discharge
2	Gums & Teeth	☐ Good	☐	Discoloration, Odor or Tartar
3	Eyes	☐ Good	☐	Clear, Hazy or Discharge
	Whites of Eyes	☐ White	☐ Red	☐ Yellow
4	Skull	☐ Good	☐	Bumps, Lumps or Pain/Sensitivity
5	Ears	☐ Good	☐	Odor, Discharge or Sensitive
6	Neck & Spine	☐ Good	☐	Lumps, Sores or Pain/Sensitivity
7	Chest & Ribs	☐ Good	☐	Lumps, Sores or Pain/Sensitivity
8	Front Legs & Paws	☐ Good	☐	Range, Cracked Pads or Broken Nails
9	Back Legs & Paws	☐ Good	☐	Range, Cracked Pads or Broken Nails
10	Abdomen	☐ Good	☐	Rigid, Pain/Odor Discharge Pain
	Genitals / Glands	☐ Good	☐	Rigid, Pain/Odor Discharge Pain
	Anal Area	☐ Good	☐	Hair, Debris or Feces
11	Skin & Coat	☐ Good	☐	Dry, Hairloss, Hot Spots or Bumps
12	Tail	☐ Good	☐	Deformity, Range of Use

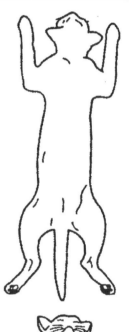

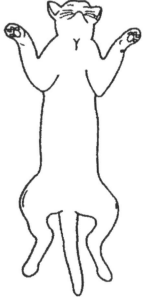

Indicate issue area(s).

VET VISITS

Date	Time
Veterinarian	
Issue	
Diagnosis	

Pulse /min	Resp. /min
Weight	Temp

Mucous Membrane Color

Medical Tests

Fecal	Urine
Blood ☐ Yes ☐ No	X-rays ☐ Yes ☐ No
Allergy Screening ☐ Yes ☐ No	
Oral Exam ☐ Yes ☐ No	

Outcome

Instructions

Notes

Date	Time
Veterinarian	
Issue	
Diagnosis	

Pulse /min	Resp. /min
Weight	Temp

Mucous Membrane Color

Medical Tests

Fecal	Urine
Blood ☐ Yes ☐ No	X-rays ☐ Yes ☐ No
Allergy Screening ☐ Yes ☐ No	
Oral Exam ☐ Yes ☐ No	

Outcome

Instructions

Notes

VET VISITS

Date	Time		Date	Time

Veterinarian

Veterinarian

Issue

Issue

Diagnosis

Diagnosis

Pulse /min	Resp. /min		Pulse /min	Resp. /min

Weight	Temp		Weight	Temp

Mucous Membrane Color

Mucous Membrane Color

Medical Tests

Medical Tests

Fecal	Urine		Fecal	Urine

Blood ☐ Yes ☐ No	X-rays ☐ Yes ☐ No		Blood ☐ Yes ☐ No	X-rays ☐ Yes ☐ No

Allergy Screening ☐ Yes ☐ No

Allergy Screening ☐ Yes ☐ No

Oral Exam ☐ Yes ☐ No

Oral Exam ☐ Yes ☐ No

Outcome

Outcome

Instructions

Instructions

Notes

Notes

VET VISITS

Date	Time		Date	Time

Veterinarian

Issue

Diagnosis

Pulse /min	Resp. /min
Weight	Temp

Mucous Membrane Color

Medical Tests

Fecal	Urine
Blood ☐ Yes ☐ No	X-rays ☐ Yes ☐ No

Allergy Screening ☐ Yes ☐ No

Oral Exam ☐ Yes ☐ No

Outcome

Instructions

Notes

Veterinarian

Issue

Diagnosis

Pulse /min	Resp. /min
Weight	Temp

Mucous Membrane Color

Medical Tests

Fecal	Urine
Blood ☐ Yes ☐ No	X-rays ☐ Yes ☐ No

Allergy Screening ☐ Yes ☐ No

Oral Exam ☐ Yes ☐ No

Outcome

Instructions

Notes

VET VISITS

Date	Time	Date	Time

Veterinarian

Issue

Diagnosis

Pulse /min	Resp. /min

Weight	Temp

Mucous Membrane Color

Medical Tests

Fecal	Urine

Blood ☐ Yes ☐ No	X-rays ☐ Yes ☐ No

Allergy Screening ☐ Yes ☐ No

Oral Exam ☐ Yes ☐ No

Outcome

Instructions

Notes

Veterinarian

Issue

Diagnosis

Pulse /min	Resp. /min

Weight	Temp

Mucous Membrane Color

Medical Tests

Fecal	Urine

Blood ☐ Yes ☐ No	X-rays ☐ Yes ☐ No

Allergy Screening ☐ Yes ☐ No

Oral Exam ☐ Yes ☐ No

Outcome

Instructions

Notes

VET VISITS

Date	Time	Date	Time

Veterinarian

Veterinarian

Issue

Issue

Diagnosis

Diagnosis

Pulse /min	Resp. /min	Pulse /min	Resp. /min
Weight	Temp	Weight	Temp
Mucous Membrane Color		Mucous Membrane Color	

Medical Tests		**Medical Tests**	
Fecal	Urine	Fecal	Urine
Blood Yes No	X-rays Yes No	Blood Yes No	X-rays Yes No
Allergy Screening Yes No		Allergy Screening Yes No	
Oral Exam Yes No		Oral Exam Yes No	

Outcome

Outcome

Instructions

Instructions

Notes

Notes

VET VISITS

Date	Time		Date	Time

Veterinarian

Issue

Diagnosis

Pulse ___ /min	Resp. ___ /min
Weight	Temp

Mucous Membrane Color

Medical Tests

Fecal	Urine
Blood ☐ Yes ☐ No	X-rays ☐ Yes ☐ No

Allergy Screening ☐ Yes ☐ No

Oral Exam ☐ Yes ☐ No

Outcome

Instructions

Notes

Veterinarian

Issue

Diagnosis

Pulse ___ /min	Resp. ___ /min
Weight	Temp

Mucous Membrane Color

Medical Tests

Fecal	Urine
Blood ☐ Yes ☐ No	X-rays ☐ Yes ☐ No

Allergy Screening ☐ Yes ☐ No

Oral Exam ☐ Yes ☐ No

Outcome

Instructions

Notes

VET VISITS

Date	Time		Date	Time

Veterinarian

Issue

Diagnosis

Pulse /min	Resp. /min
Weight	Temp

Mucous Membrane Color

Medical Tests

Fecal	Urine

Blood ☐ Yes ☐ No   X-rays ☐ Yes ☐ No

Allergy Screening ☐ Yes ☐ No

Oral Exam ☐ Yes ☐ No

Outcome

Instructions

Notes

Veterinarian

Issue

Diagnosis

Pulse /min	Resp. /min
Weight	Temp

Mucous Membrane Color

Medical Tests

Fecal	Urine

Blood ☐ Yes ☐ No   X-rays ☐ Yes ☐ No

Allergy Screening ☐ Yes ☐ No

Oral Exam ☐ Yes ☐ No

Outcome

Instructions

Notes

SURGERIES

Date

Time

Veterinarian

Surgical Procedure

Post-Op Instructions

Medication(s)

Notes

Date / Time	Surgical Site OK	Observations
	☐ Yes ☐ No	
	☐ Yes ☐ No	
	☐ Yes ☐ No	
	☐ Yes ☐ No	
	☐ Yes ☐ No	
	☐ Yes ☐ No	
	☐ Yes ☐ No	
	☐ Yes ☐ No	
	☐ Yes ☐ No	
	☐ Yes ☐ No	
	☐ Yes ☐ No	
	☐ Yes ☐ No	

SURGERIES

Date	Time	Veterinarian

Surgical Procedure

Post-Op Instructions

Medication(s)

Notes

Date / Time	Surgical Site OK	Observations
	Yes No	
	Yes No	
	Yes No	
	Yes No	
	Yes No	
	Yes No	
	Yes No	
	Yes No	
	Yes No	
	Yes No	
	Yes No	
	Yes No	

SURGERIES

Date	Time	Veterinarian

Surgical Procedure

Post-Op Instructions

Medication(s)

Notes

Date / Time	Surgical Site OK	Observations
	Yes No	
	Yes No	
	Yes No	
	Yes No	
	Yes No	
	Yes No	
	Yes No	
	Yes No	
	Yes No	
	Yes No	
	Yes No	
	Yes No	

SURGERIES

Date	Time	Veterinarian

Surgical Procedure

Post-Op Instructions

Medication(s)

Notes

Date / Time	Surgical Site OK	Observations
	Yes No	
	Yes No	
	Yes No	
	Yes No	
	Yes No	
	Yes No	
	Yes No	
	Yes No	
	Yes No	
	Yes No	
	Yes No	
	Yes No	

MILESTONES

Milestone	Age	Date	Notes
Car Ride			
Walk			
Bath			
Litterbox Trained			
Trip To Vet			
Snout-To-Tail			
Toilet Trained			
Certifications			
Trainings			

MILESTONES

Milestone	Age	Date	Notes

Photo Here (4x6 inches)

Photo Here (4x6 inches)

SPECIAL MOMENTS

Date	Time	Location

Description

Date	Time	Location

Description

Photo Here (4x6 inches)

Photo Here (4x6 inches)

SPECIAL MOMENTS

Date	Time	Location

Description

Date	Time	Location

Description

Photo Here (4x6 inches)

Photo Here (4x6 inches)

SPECIAL MOMENTS

Date	Time	Location

Description

Date	Time	Location

Description

Photo Here (4x6 inches)

Photo Here (4x6 inches)

SPECIAL MOMENTS

Date

Time

Location

Description

Date

Time

Location

Description

Photo Here (4x6 inches)

Photo Here (4x6 inches)

SPECIAL MOMENTS

Date	Time	Location

Description

Date	Time	Location

Description

Photo Here (4x6 inches)

Photo Here (4x6 inches)

SPECIAL MOMENTS

Date	Time	Location

Description

Date	Time	Location

Description

Photo Here (4x6 inches)

Photo Here (4x6 inches)

SPECIAL MOMENTS

Date	Time	Location

Description

Date	Time	Location

Description

ANSWER KEY

Cat First Aid Quiz Page 15

1. TRUE, Pet First Aid is the **immediate care** given to a cat who is injured or suddenly takes ill.

2. FALSE, all human medicines **do not** work on cats if you adjust the dosage for their weight. **Many human medicines can be harmful and/ or ineffective on cats. Always check with your veterinarian about all medications.**

3. TRUE, as a general rule, normal temperature for cats ranges from **100.4° to 102.5° F.**

4. TRUE, Pet CPR is best learned with **hands-on training and skills practice.**

5. FALSE, Rescue Breathing is **not** warranted when your pet has no heart beat and no breathing. **This situation requires Cat CPR.**

6. FALSE, the Primary Pet Assessment **does not include** the skills and techniques necessary for Pet CPR, First Aid and Rescue Breathing. **To learn these skills we highly recommend our PetSaver™ training. Visit PetTech.net for more information and to book a class today.**

7. TRUE, if you suspect your cat is poisoned, it's important to **immediately get your cat to the vet,** as well as **know what and how much poison was ingested.**

8. FALSE, the Black Widow Spider bite **can be very harmful to cats and requires vet attention.**

9. FALSE, death by poisoning is one of the **most** common preventable cat accidents. **Take the time to secure any household products and plants that are dangerous for cats.**

10. TRUE, baby snake venom **is as venomous** as their parent's venom.

11. FALSE, Lilies **are** one of the many plants that are poisonous to cats. **The entire lily plant is toxic: the stem, leaves, flowers, pollen, and even the water in a vase can cause fatal kidney failure in less than 3 days.**

Cat Traits Word Search Page 16

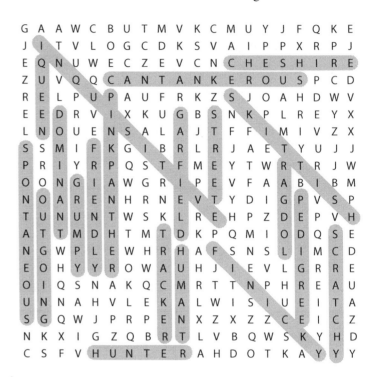

Spot 8 Differences Page 17

ANSWER KEY

Doggy Maze Page 18

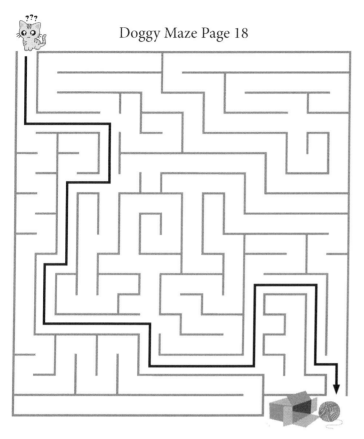

Cat Adoption Logic Puzzle Page 20

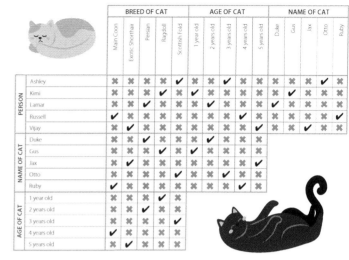

		BREED OF CAT					AGE OF CAT					NAME OF CAT				
		Main Coon	Exotic Shorthair	Persian	Ragdoll	Scottish Fold	1 year old	2 years old	3 years old	4 years old	5 years old	Duke	Gus	Jax	Otto	Ruby
PERSON	Ashley	✗	✗	✗	✗	✓	✗	✗	✓	✗	✗	✗	✗	✗	✓	✗
	Kimi	✗	✗	✗	✓	✗	✓	✗	✗	✗	✗	✗	✓	✗	✗	✗
	Lamar	✗	✗	✓	✗	✗	✗	✗	✗	✗	✗	✓	✗	✗	✗	✗
	Russell	✓	✗	✗	✗	✗	✗	✗	✗	✗	✗	✗	✗	✗	✗	✓
	Vijay	✗	✓	✗	✗	✗	✗	✗	✗	✗	✗	✗	✗	✓	✗	✗
NAME OF CAT	Duke	✗	✗	✗	✗	✗	✗	✗	✗	✗	✗					
	Gus	✗	✗	✗	✓	✗	✓	✗	✗	✗	✗					
	Jax	✗	✓	✗	✗	✗	✗	✗	✗	✗	✓					
	Otto	✗	✗	✗	✗	✓	✗	✗	✓	✗	✗					
	Ruby	✓	✗	✗	✗	✗	✗	✗	✗	✓	✗					
AGE OF CAT	1 year old	✗	✗	✗	✓	✗										
	2 years old	✗	✗	✓	✗	✗										
	3 years old	✗	✗	✗	✗	✓										
	4 years old	✓	✗	✗	✗	✗										
	5 years old	✗	✓	✗	✗	✗										

Find The 6 Cats Page 19

Snout-To-Tail Word Scramble Page 21

Snout and Muzzle — Gums and Teeth — Eyes

Skull — Ears — Neck and Spine

Chest and Ribs — Front Legs and Paws — Back Legs and Paws

Abdomen — Skin and Coat — Tail

LOST CAT

We know how difficult it is to have a missing cat, but don't panic!

Every pet parent's greatest fear is having a missing cat. Going by the numbers, only 18% of all indoor cats will go missing during their life-time. The good news is 75% of missing cats are eventually reunited with their pet parents. Cats generally don't go far, they tend to stay in a 3-4 house radius, as long as they have a warm and dry place to hide.

Best chance of recovery is with preparedness and quick action within the first 12 hours. Also, investing in a GPS tracker can drastically help you track down your missing cat. We use and personally recommend: https://amzn.to/3f5EiLe

WHAT TO DO IF YOUR CAT GOES MISSING

1. Start your search immediately.

2. Double check the home and immediate area.

3. Begin in the immediate area that the cat disappeared and expand out from there.

4. Enlist the help of friends, family, and neighbors.

5. Make sure someone is at home base in case the cat returns.

6. Download and fill out the Help! Missing Cat Poster: www.PetTech.net/missingpet

7. Make copies and post around your neighborhood.
   Note, try to use photo that shows collar color as it can help identify your missing cat.

8. Utilize social media!

HELP! MISSING CAT

| CAT NAME | Charlie | COLOR | Orange |
| AGE | 2 years | COLLAR | Red |

PLEASE CONTACT:

987-654-3210   jen221@mail.com

REWARD

Made in the USA
Monee, IL
26 March 2023

1582e00a-b675-4834-a729-7147c3f010b8R01